The JOURNEY

Original Title:

CONTINUATION OF A LEGEND

The Jottings of a Young Man

Translated from the Russian by
William E. Butler

TRANSNATIONAL PUBLISHERS, INC.
Dobbs Ferry, New York

HORIZON/New Horizon Press Publishers
New York, New York

Distributors

To Libraries:
Transnational Publishers, Inc., P.O. Box 7282, Ardsley-on-Hudson, New York, NY 10503.

To the Trade:
New Horizon Press Publishers, 156 Fifth Avenue, New York, NY 10010.

Book Information

Joint edition by: Transnational Publishers, Inc., and New Horizon Press Publishers

Library of Congress Cataloging in Publication Data

Anatoliĭ, A., 1929–1979.
    The journey.

    Translation of: Prodolzhenie legendy.
    "Original title: Continuation of a legend:
the jottings of a young man."
    I. Title.   II. Title: Continuation of a legend.
PG3478.N34P713   1984   891.73'44   84-99
ISBN: 0-941320-20-0 Transnational Publishers, Inc.
        0-88282-300-0 New Horizon Press Publishers

Manufactured in the United States of America

CONTENTS

THE SECOND NOTEBOOK

End of the Second Notebook

THE THIRD NOTEBOOK

End of the Third Notebook

THE FOURTH NOTEBOOK

THE BEGINNING OF THE NEXT NOTEBOOK

TRANSLATION NOTE

Anatolii Kuznetsov (1929–1979) is best known as the author of *Babi Yar*, the documentary novel based on the German atrocities during the Second World War near Kiev. His initial success and reputation as a writer, however, were based on the present tale, *Continuation of a Legend*, first published in a newly-established monthly journal of the Union of Writers, *Iunost'*, no. 7 (July 1957), pp. 6-59 and immediately thereafter in book form with minor revisions, including Soviet translations into English and Spanish. The present translation is based on the redaction published at Novosibirsk in 1967.

Kuznetsov was born in the outskirts of Kiev, at Kurenevka. As a twelve-year old in occupied Kiev, he experienced first-hand the terrors and privations of war, including being an eye-witness of the mass executions at *Babi Yar* only a half-mile or so from his home; twice he escaped being sent to Germany and began writing at the age of fourteen his impressions of the German occupation. When Kiev was liberated, he helped rebuild his school, studied at the ballet school attached to the Kiev opera, and later at the Russian dramatic theatre. As a schoolboy he won prizes at the city and union republic level, including in 1946 a literary competition for a series of short stories. In 1952 he went to work on the construction of the Kakhova Hydroelectric Station on the

Dnieper, where he was a carpenter, road-worker, and journalist. He finished the tenth grade at night school in 1954 and enrolled at the Gorky Institute of Literature. A year later he became a member of the Communist Party. In 1956 he joined the staff of *Iunost'*. On assignment he travelled to the Irkutsk and Bratsk hydroelectric stations . . .

Continuation of a Legend is an account in essay form of his experiences and the individuals he met. He did travel from Moscow to Irkutsk on the "third shelf" with a group of lads recruited to work at Bratsk. Dima, Grishka, Vasek, and Lesha were real people of the background and character described. Once at Irkutsk the author did join the Anna Moskalenko Brigade as a concrete worker—she too was real and so were her accomplishments—and observed the reflooding by the Angara. Even the author's experience at the Kakhova construction site was insufficient to enable him to endure the pace at Irkutsk, and he did end up in hospital. His neighbor there was the Buriat, Misha, who had indeed been stabbed while coming to the aid of an unknown woman. The names, events, and chronology are consequently as they were. The main hero, however, is fictional, invented, the author says, from beginning to end but obliged to undergo all the reversals of fortune that Kuznetsov himself did. Those portrayed in the work continued to stay in touch with the author at least up to the mid-1960s: Valia Fedorova had become an engineer; crane operators Misha and Efremovich worked on at other construction sites; Leshka apparently remained a thief, or so he reported in one letter to the author.

The talent which reached its fullest expression in *Babi Yar* is much in evidence in this widely acclaimed work, as too are certain enduring elements of Soviet life. Siberia continues to charm, fascinate, and challenge all who visit or work there. Mastery of that vast expanse has become an integral part of Soviet folklore, a theme of Soviet literature, journalism, art, ballet, and even opera, to an extent little appreciated in the West. Kuznetsov explores two other themes just emerging in the mid-1950s as larger societal concerns. One was what came to be known as the unwarranted separation in the Soviet view between "school" and "life," a concern that in the late 1950s and early 1960s led to far-reaching reforms in Soviet secondary and higher education and promises to do so again in 1984. Another is the hero's intolerance of and distaste for "parasitism" in Soviet life. In the late 1950s anti-parasite legislation was introduced in the Soviet union republics to combat the phenomenon, and although that legislation ultimately had to be jettisoned for inherent defects of its own, the duty to work, and the moral qualities associated with socially useful labor, continue to be prominent in Soviet life, literature, and law.

As for the "legend," the fable of Angara and Enisei is a multidimensional backdrop for restless souls, imaginary or real, past or present, who rise up out of their homes or existences to seek identity, fortune, or adventure elsewhere. In 1969 Anatolii Kuznetsov was granted asylum in London while on a visit to gather material for a book.

THE FIRST NOTEBOOK

ON THE ROAD

Who invented the word "maturity"? Who first thought to issue a maturity certificate to naive kids after finishing school? As though life could be changed in a single day by a paper.

I had graduated from the tenth grade*, but never in my life had I felt so confused. So helpless. A puppy.

I shall tell no one of this. I write in my diary because it is so difficult and terrifying for me. For ten years they told us that all paths were open. And it turns out they are closed. Why were we deceived and trained for the easy life?

From nursery school we, moving our mommies to tears, were taught to sing: "For the young the road is everywhere," but aged seventeen we see there is only one road: to the factory, to hard sloggers, to the fuel dump! We need no one and are of no interest to anyone.

Well, fair enough, I did hate German and trigonometry. Should I have

---

* (schooling in the Soviet Union, primary and secondary, normally begins at age 7 and consists of 10 grades—transl.)

1

had to lie and say that I liked them, to be evasive, to prepare cribs, and to cram in order to earn my A's? I didn't cram. I ploughed through history by chance. And for this, with two B's and a C on my diploma, I receive a kind invitation to the virgin lands or to be a bootblack. Fool!—to aspire to an Institute without a medal?

Thank you.

It's so distressing. What will be, will be? I found myself somewhere in a field, in darkness, in the rain, no light visible, a certificate of "maturity" pasted on my forehead. This is how I enter life. What is to be done? What is to be done?

Viktor applied to a Polytechnic; he hopes for something, sits, desperately crams trigonometry. In my view this is cowardice.

Iuna—that will pass, I'm sure. Having understood this, I also understood that we shan't go on together.

TWENTY-THREE HOUR DAYS

Six people are travelling in our train compartment. That's good: seven and eight often travel in a compartment. Every twenty-four hours an hour is lost, where no one knows. We move eastward, toward the sun.

The railway operates according to Moscow time, and for a long time the Muscovite passengers are confused about the hours.

"Are you going to bed already? What time is it?"

"Twelve midnight."

"Not really! By what time?"

"Local time."

"Oh! Well, then let's sit down for supper. We still live by Moscow time."

Our conductor is loud, red-headed, slovenly—Uncle Kostia. He doesn't sit quietly for a moment—walks, shouts, likes to sit down at the small tables briefly, and stares, stares with his colorless piercing eyes. He has a brass wristwatch almost as large as an alarm clock. It ticks as though small brass hammers within were beating on an anvil. Uncle Kostia is proud of it, scorns all others, and gladly allows all who desire to "listen":

"What kind of watch do you have? This is a watch? Mine was a gift—I won't take it. Listen to mine, nine jewels. Chronometer!"

We also orientated ourselves by this chronometer.

Uncle Kostia acknowledges no time zones except railway time. But all the same it turned out that when travelling home to Vladivostok he moved the hands seven hours ahead and lived for several days "off" like all good people on local time and didn't even wear a uniform. When, for the sake of principle, he tried to live at home on "standard" time it proved to be very inconvenient—to go to bed when everyone else was waking up. And, moreover, in Vladivostok the beer halls are closing when, Moscow-time, it is 4:00 a.m.

However, this concession to the laws of nature was a minor one, since Uncle Kostia wasn't at home much. Bring the pay packet, stay for a while, thrash his son for a D, and getting back on the train for a fortnight, the watch seven hours behind, on the road again . . .

Five of my neighbors are not like me. They were "recruited." I'm still completely naive and stupid. I'd heard of centers for the "organized recruitment of workers," seen advertisements, but didn't understand how they concerned me. I didn't know that there was no reason to buy a ticket at one's own expense to travel into the unknown. Everywhere there are authorized persons with whom you conclude a contract for three years, and they issue you moving expenses, a *per diem*, and free travel. For Siberia and the virgin lands there likewise is recruitment through the Komsomol district committees . . .

On our Moscow-Vladivostok train there are a hundred such "recruited" kids; I, the 101st, travel at my own expense. True, I have one essential advantage: I am not bound by any contractual obligations and can quietly take off at any time.

Five full days to Irkutsk. The railway carriages are fine—made entirely of metal, comfortable, with mirrors and "compulsory ventilation" (when I asked what the inscription on the metal plate meant, Uncle Kostia explained "Whether you want it or not, there is ventilation"). But all the same to loaf about for five days in this stuffy cage is unbearably boring, stifling, and we want to be "ventilated" constantly. I have already said that our car is, in railway terminology, a "merry" one. At each stop it is besieged by peasant women with bundles and children, by some sort of migrants, speculators. The passengers are all squeezed together and constantly moving about. The aisles are congested with belongings. One must have the energy and throat of Uncle Kostia in order to cope with this bazaar of yelling, pushing passengers: some are boarding, others getting off, this one has no ticket, that one is intoxicated, one washes diapers in the toilet and a threatening queue has gathered at the door . . .

Our amusements? Leshka has beslobbered, floppy playing cards, and for hours we six play "Durak."

A deaf and dumb woman sold home-made postcards in the car. She offered them covertly and to men only. From the adjacent compartment peered a crone who also wanted to take a look. My, how the deaf and dumb lady snarled at her: Keep your nose out of other people's business!

Because there were half-naked women on the postcards, not ours, but foreign types, in picturesque poses with captions: "Wait for me and I shall reappear like the sun after a shower," "Devotion and love I sacredly keep" or verses:

> "Ah, why are we parted,
> Ah, why do we live apart?
> Is it not time to marry,
> To value love!"

Since we don't throw money away, we merely looked. But Uncle Kostia bought a magnificently built painted lady, with curls like a sheep, encircled by pigeons holding letters in their beaks, and a whole orangerie of

4

flowers which grow, no doubt, on Mars; the caption proclaimed: "Our next meeting is Sunday." We delicately began to sound out for whom this piquant postcard was intended, and elicited it. It turned out that Uncle Kostia had a "spare" wife at the other end of the line, in Moscow, on Savel'ev Lane. Both wives know about one another's existence, even exchanged messages, and each in turn squabbles with Uncle Kostia so that basically he rested on the road, mercifully a long one. How long did he expect to live?

"The end is not in sight . . ."

"Well then how do they share you?"

"They can go to hell. One collects the advance on earnings and the other, the pay packet."

The deaf and dumb woman went into the adjacent compartment, the lads can not contain themselves and follow after her, to look . . . Loud laughter and obscene noises emanate from there.

And then melancholy began to torture me.

Iuna doubtless already is going to tutorial consultations. Soon she will have examinations. And what awaits me?

Even now I don't understand how I ventured to board the train, to depart having no acquaintances and no idea what I would do in Siberia and whether I was of use to anyone in general. Perhaps I did it because mother had cried and implored me to take a job in a children's toy artel:* "They require someone, and it is close and convenient. You will work like all people do."

Like all people? That means: to bring your pay packet home, to go to the movies on Saturdays, and on Sundays to play dominos in the yard or to build a pen for the little pig, and finally to marry, if possible a dressmaker. In the sixth grade we dreamed of faraway seas.

Iuna! Iunka . . . But what can I say?

The train goes so fast, rolls and shakes so much, that it is almost impossible to write.

* (small cooperative organizations of artisans—transl.)

FROM THE GREY HAIRS OF DAYS PAST

We were three. Sasha, Viktor, and I.

In school they called us the "Three Musketeers" and the "Three Tank Crew Members," but the latter we rejected because only Viktor had drawn tanks in notebooks from the first grade. Sasha drew airplanes, and I, ships.

If one of us was "taken ill" by something, the illness was instantaneously transmitted to the others. Vic's father gave him a camera, and we three all became photographers. Sasha mastered a crystal set—our pockets were filled with bulbs, condensers, and wires. I kept rabbits—and on one fine day Vic's mama discovered cabbage and grass under the piano and a rabbit hutch in a box under the radio, for which Vic was then in trouble—ouch!

Vic saw the film "The Young Guard" six times; I, nine; and Sasha, fifteen. Until the eighth grade we were terrified of girls, and in the ninth all three were in love with Iuna. Jealousy led to a quarrel between Viktor and Sasha—and thereafter our friendship faded.

No, it was not Iuna, but something else.

For example, the Communist Youth League.

We joined the Komsomol together, all three terribly excited, and Vic declared this first step was our most important: a Komsomol member advanced in life more easily, and he achieved more than a "non-joiner." Everything began from this. What does it mean to advance? And in the name of what do we exist in general? We argued throughout the evening, having forgotten about homework.

Sasha said if one had to be like Aleksandr Matrosov, he would, because the word "Motherland" was sacred to him. Vic spitefully asked: and when would the Motherland give him a new apartment? Because Sasha lived with his father in an old dilapidated house, in a tiny room with a rotten floor, and they were promised and promised, but never moved.

Sasha was the tallest of us, ungainly, and the first to begin to talk with a bass voice; and in his behavior, the most straightforward. Having decided to do something, he persisted until he achieved it. He was the only one of us who learned to photograph with professional skill, became a short-wave radio operator, and received postcards from radio operators all over the world. His father worked at a brake factory, and Sasha often went there to turn needed parts, made a vise for himself, and equipped a shop in the storeroom.

It was always pleasant to go there: a tiny room under the stairs, in semi-darkness—a heap of iron plates, nuts, wires, the smell of acid, on the bench a neighbor's disemboweled radio receiver, broken cuckoo clocks, a television picture tube, metal filings, and through a tiny window a patch of sky is visible and the adjacent fire proof wall with pigeons on it.

There we also assembled to argue. There was nowhere at our home, and although Viktor's parents had a large apartment and a dacha outside the city and they even had allotted Vic an individual "study," for some reason it seemed bleak to us. But here we could shout, uninhibited, and argue until we were hoarse. Sasha made things at the same time. When carried away, he soldered something unnecessarily, vexedly chucked the soldering iron, and shook his fists.

More often he went at it with feeling and swore. Vic tired himself out with lively examples and arguments. I in turn went from one side to the other.

Vic began to call Sasha a "patriot without pants;" he was answered more maliciously: "a rat without a motherland."

And after Vic had spoken very badly, cynically, of Iuna, and Sasha broke a precious television tube on his head, they openly came to hate one another and lashed one another with caustic ridicule when they met.

Vic and I were enamored with collecting old coins—Sasha didn't join us. He took up with new friends from among the factory kids. Sasha didn't invite me to visit. Perhaps because before examinations one never engaged in extraneous matters.

I spent whole days with Vic in his "study" reviewing physics and chemistry with him. Once we decided to rest, went to a shish-kebab restaurant like fully grown people, and Vic taught me to make "ersha" by mixing beer, wine, and vodka; we imagined we were drinking cocktails. We were so drunk that we disgraced ourselves; then we searched for Iuna's house for a long time in order to pay our respects but happily did not find it, and then somehow found ourselves in Vic's "study" where we slept on the carpet until morning. At home mother greeted me with tears; she already had called the police . . .

. . . No, all that is past. And nothing to sort out. Our paths finally diverged from Sasha's; I don't even know whether he is getting ready to enroll somewhere. Vic moved out of the city at once to prepare for examinations; I left and didn't see him. On the day of departure I received a letter from him which I re-read lying on the third berth of the Moscow-Vladivostok train—that is all that remains with me of the past.

LETTER FROM VIKTOR

"Dear Tolia!

Are you not aware how melancholy I am? The sines don't stay in my head. All about me—stylish kids, girls in trousers zip along the street on bicycles, play volleyball, dance in the evenings to the tape recorder—in a word, distracted regardless of the consequences. I am alone among them, like an idiot I sit and cram cotangents, provoking ridicule.

Who needs it? Why does my fate depend on these confounded cotangents which I would rather not see for evermore nor know—and would live well without them? Our passion for the radio is to blame for everything—papa imagined that this was my vocation and strongly pushes me toward a Polytechnic, the radio faculty. But honestly I don't know what I want nor what my calling is. O.K. Papa insists on the Polytechnic—I go. If he insisted on Architecture—I also would go . . . A nasty story.

But listen, are you right to simply withdraw from the struggle. That is panic! That's even worse than my "don't know what I want." So what? I have two C's on my diploma and where do less than A's go—what does this resolve?

Your cowardly (pardon) venture to flee where eyes cannot follow does not appeal to me. I thought a great deal about it. Came to the conclusion not to give up. Listen Tolia, do your best instead to enroll in a Polytechnic! You too are entranced by radio sets. We two will be happier, look after one another, and stick it out, prepare cribs. One must struggle! One must believe!

Be aware that only the most adaptable and tenacious survive in life. One must courageously press on! If you cannot proceed straight ahead, re-organize yourself, adapt, but go on at any price. Hear me—any price! This is the only thing I know and that I presently believe in.

Tolia, I am not as frank with anyone as I am with you. I was with Sasha—but that's in the past. And now especially I miss your questions, your anxious casting about. I don't chat with anyone. Our dacha settlement consists of such, I tell you, philistines—well-matched! No doubt they operate on the principle "a fisherman sees a fisherman from afar." Who they don't see are: self-satisfied mugs, proprietors, cynics. And their children are the same.

Observing them, I think: is it possible there exists in the world any honor, any struggle for ideas, truth, or good? Among our neighbors (and even in our family) this commodity is not rated.

The owner of the luxurious dacha on the right is the manager of some snack-bar "spot." The even more luxurious and tasteless dacha on the left belongs to the manager of a supply section of some trust. And on the edge of the settlement—laughter!—a brand new dacha built by—whom do you think? A beggar who walks along the electric trains with a blind wife: "Citizens, before you are two disabled persons. During the war, I . . . etc. Give something for sustenance." Did we not ride together with you and give him something "for sustenance?"

Look and think, are not desperate loners engaged in a game of integrity, which they also obscure—they see neither human life, nor dachas, nor the light of God? People sacrificing themselves. Who needs these victims?

9

What do you think? Sasha I would not ask, I know his opinion; he is a convinced victim. And you?

Tolia, come to me. We'll talk, think, study for examinations. Tell me how Iuna is getting on. Come!

I will firmly take your hand. I wait!"

Yes . . . wait, Vic. I will come "soon."

A LONG ROAD AND A REVENUE BUILDING

But for some reason Siberia fails to appear. Out the windows the same landscape: fields, forests, thickets, riverlets, and fields again. We crossed the Urals and failed to notice it was the Urals. No mountains, no menacing rocks, merely a hilly area. Not far from the Chusovoi River a simple striped pillar was fleetingly glimpsed at one of the stations—that was the boundary between Europe and Asia.

Asia!

At the stops the entire train jumps off to stretch their legs on the platform. At the bazaars they buy fermented boiled milk, fried chicken, and hot potatoes in newspaper bags. And if the train stopped at an isolated siding, one may pick flowers or find mushrooms or wild strawberries two steps from the track, or play ball.

At one station vagrant gypsies assaulted the train. Filthy, wiry, picturesque, with heaps of half-naked kids and lazy dogs, they were going somewhere, having some purpose of their own.

I never did understand them. What strength resided in those black, strong men, their dark-complexioned and boney wives, what makes them move, move?

They don't know today what they will eat tomorrow, they are freezing, soaked, humiliated, and they beg, but try to suggest they join a children's toy artel! How unconcerned they must be about something, which I don't understand, in order to live so simply, "like birds in the sky," without perishing and

10

without tranquility. One is afraid to undertake a single trip, thinks it over and over, leaves oneself a loophole to escape just in case. But they wander and roam. Not working, nor sowing, nor harvesting, but they live, being born and dying on the road.

"Young and handsome, let me tell your fortune! Place a ruble on your palm and I'll tell you the whole truth."*

A policeman blew his whistle. The gypsy girls fled, dived under the cars, and again climbed up with desperate impudence. Perhaps because the stop was only for five minutes.

One dreadful old woman pestered me. She had black, chapped bare feet, and she shuffled along the concrete platform, shaking her countless petticoats, followed me along the entire train, running from one side to the other.

"Place a ruble on your palm. Oh, what a mean one! Give to a poor gypsy for some bread. I'll tell you the whole truth!"

I felt embarrassed and ill. She virtually implored:

"Do you want me to tell where you have your money? Right in this pocket. There it is!"

This did not strike me as a joke: the money lay precisely in my right pocket. Only later did I understand that involuntarily I must have held my hand on this pocket.

I should have driven her away but lacked the character to do so. I gave her three rubles and thus learned that before me stood a long road, interests in a revenue building, near me a queen of diamonds, but in her mind, a king of hearts. After this, she plucked a hair from me, placed it on a mirror, and demanded three rubles more. Happily, the train began to move.

The gypsy lady had excited me, and I could not forget for a long time the bare chapped feet on the concrete and the wailing: "I'll tell the whole truth!" A poor word, "truth," who does not shred it to pieces.

We travelled for five stops or so, and then I resolved not lightheartedly

* (all prices are given in the pre-1961 monetary reform levels. To approximate modern values, divide by ten. 1 ruble equals 100 kopecks—transl.)

11

that to live in the world as a parasite is an abomination. And that if in the world there were no such beggars, sellers of postcards, fortune-tellers, the world would become a bit cleaner, better . . .

Oh, old woman, old woman! It wasn't difficult to guess we all were on a long road, that each of us had business in the revenue building, and that each had a queen of diamonds in his heart. We all are the same, even though we all are very different.

WHO WE ARE

For the third day the wheels hammer. The kilometers number already in the thousands, hundreds of games had been played, dozens of glasses of tea had been drunk, and we had become accustomed to one another, gotten used to each other.

VASEK: a mischievous, sharp lad, he is my neighbor on the democratic third berth. Slender, easy, vociferous, he likes poems, adores climbing beneath the ceiling and sings lengthy songs. Vasek is afraid of nothing in life except policemen. Only a deaf grandma remained at home, whose life he "disturbed;" he had gone to Siberia not for the money, nor for a warm place, nor for the glory, but simply for the desire to see different lands.

He had no belongings whatever with him: a jacket and a bag of rusk. Like a sparrow: he went into a station, bought a glass of blueberries or nuts, pecked—and was satisfied. Vasek is a great visionary. He heard from his neighbor, a soldier, that in Mogilev, where he had served, "Life is pure paradise: two rubles for a meter of sausage"—this pleased him and he dreamed up a whole fairytale:

"Tol', hey Tol'! And in this country stands a tree, and on it cookies grow. At the top fresh sponge cakes, warm ones , , , and at the bottom, dry Napoleons. Terrific, huh?"

"Sleep, imp!"

12

"And a stick is driven into the tree; on it sits a parrot reading verses by Dolmatovskii. And we devour cookies and say to him: "Polly is a fool!"

Vasek has no secrets; his life is an open book, and the whole car knows that his entire capital is seventy rubles, and his grandma is not malicious but only scolds day and night and pondered marriage. Everyone is nice to him, teaches him some common sense, and feeds him a bit. Vasek affably accepts both the lessons and a slice of buttered roll. He is blissfully happy on the third berth; there is his kingdom: he can twirl the ventilators and generally live his own life.

IVAN BUGAI: In the general combined cars, as is well-known, the lowest berths are for "sitting" and the middle are reserved seat tickets. Bugai had paid the supplement from his own money for one reserved seat.

He has a toothache. He travelled from a collective farm in a car, a dental abscess had swollen and his right cheek had so puffed up that it was terrible to look at. Ivan Bugai—*nomen est omen*—is huge, slow, and slow-witted. The berth beneath him creaks, and it becomes uncomfortable to sit below it.

As a thrifty traveller, Bugai took a large shaggy leather jacket with him on the trip. He sleeps on this department store sheepskin coat, buries himself in it, lays one sleeve under his head and covers the dental abscess with the other, having turned it inside out.

Ivan Bugai is a quiet, reliable man of integrity. He finished nine grades in a rural school, read about the construction sites in Siberia, gave up as a bad job the ritual lamentations and persuasions of his mother and aunts, was recruited, and left home in disgrace. He worked in a collective farm smithy and earned some cash, and therefore allows himself a luxury: he goes to the dining car, sits there, and drinks beer.

On the very first day Ivan's watch was stolen. The watch was an old one on a wide worn-out band. Bugai woke up in the morning, wiped his eyes with his hand, and the severed band fell on the shelf. Bugai threw it out the window, scratched himself, and calmed down. On his wrist only a white untanned strip remained.

Bugai had a green veneered suitcase with a heavy padlock. The lid was cov-

13

ered inside with color photographs of weightlifters neatly cut out from *Ogenok*, and the suitcase itself was full of nourishment, both physical and spiritual: loaves, tomatoes, and tenth grade textbooks. Bugai was resolved to finish the tenth year in Siberia at night school.

He could rapturously cite various large statistics reflecting national economic achievements but doesn't find patient listeners.

Then he retrieves tomatoes from a suitcase and slices them on the table, invites Vasek, and, opening the *Economic Geography of the USSR*, recounts to him in detail the capacity of the Irkutsk Hydroelectric Power Station—600,000 kilowatts, and the Bratsk Hydroelectric Power Station—3,200,000 kilowatts. Vasek eats tomatoes and listens gladly.

GRIGORII: A soldier occupied the second sleeping place in our compartment. He left at Kirov, and Grisha seized the berth immediately. He sits there all the time and is apprehensive lest the conductor remember the place is free and turn him out.

Grishka is avaricious and a kulak.* He has a pock-marked timorous face and greedy hands. He overloaded the berth at once with bundles, suitcases, distributed everything under his back and head so they would not be stolen, with scarcely space for himself among his wealth.

Grigorii is least interested of all in the capacity of the stations on the Angara. He listens avidly to stories about unbelievable earnings at construction sites, and at night, when everyone is asleep, he recalculates the advance payment issued to him. I can see this from above. In his trousers a small money-bag dangles on a string. He also has a watch—a silver pocket-watch with a massive chain—and fumbles for it ten times every night.

He buys nothing at stations, doesn't even get off: he guards his stuff. But for us this is handy: we calmly go for a walk, having charged him to champion the compartment against new lodgers. Grisha is truly ready to fall in battle,

* (literally "fist," the term designates loosely the middle and upper class peasantry, many of whom were liquidated in the early 1930s during the collectivization of agriculture—transl.)

swears that a bandit gang is travelling here, and so frightens the passengers that half the car looks askance at us with terror.

When we sit down to eat, Grigorii moves to the side and pretends he wants nothing. We call him, he refuses, and then reluctantly sits down. But since he is always hungry, he begins to devour his meal like a wolf. He never contributes his own food. Bugai demonstratively throws down his loaves and breathes scornfully, and Vasek chokes with laughter and hides behind a newspaper.

Grishka left at home his father and stepmother and five brothers and sisters. He speaks well of his stepmother: she is thrifty. And his father, a proprietor. They live well. But the holding is his father's, not Grisha's. And it is time for Grisha to marry soon. They say a decent wage can be earned in Siberia. Some friends in Verkhnecharsk signed up, and so did Grigorii.

FAT LESHKA: Beneath "Grisha's reserved seat" on the bottom berth Leshka is sprawled out like a lord. Actually, it's all the same to him where he sits and on what he sleeps. Whether it were a mountain of suitcases or a woodpile, he would settle down on it with the same comfort. He is fat, and everything is soft to him, even without a bed.

Leshka's face is round, chubby, and always shines like the sun. He is reddish, good-natured, and phlegmatic. He sits sprawled out, looks at everyone, and smiles. He loves to play checkers, and for this purpose has a squared sheet in his pocket and twenty-four buttons.

His pockets are remarkable: in them are glasses, an ashtray, a can-opener, a scarf, and a number of nails of various sizes. It turned out he also had playing cards, but he plays not to win, merely to enjoy the game. He both trumps and draws with enjoyment, but most of all he likes to cheat. He trumps a trump with a non-trump card and smiles: did they notice or not? From time to time Grigorii loses control, goes for him like a rooster, searches for and pulls out some sixes secreted "on a sling" somewhere. Leshka takes no offence—on the contrary, he is quite content.

And we were startled having suddenly learned that our Leshka had been imprisoned for six months for a brawl. Smiling bashfully, Leshka related how

15

he once while drunk badly beat someone up and was tried. Thereafter he was given no peace in the village, and he went on to other places.

He has a father and a mother. His dress is almost foppish: a cracked-leather jacket and chromium boots. He has no baggage at all unless you count what he has in his pockets.

However, he did acquire baggage en route. On the second day we went to eat in the restaurant car. Leshka returned together with everyone and modestly lay down in his place. But something bothered him: he tossed, turned, sighed. Then he got up, dug into his pockets and pulled out three glasses, three spoons, and a fork. Vasek roared with laughter. Grigorii waved his arms like a broody hen and jumped to conceal this "wealth." Bugai sniffed, quietly took them away, returned them to the dining car, and silently slipped them on the table. Lesha smiled for awhile, took no offence at all, and calmly slept. In the evening he brought two glasses with the glass-holders.

In fact, he had no need of them. He simply regretted that such fine things were left on the table unguarded. The ashtray which he took from his pocket was ceramic, but those in the dining car were glass—he had picked it up somewhere previously. First we swore, shamed him, took the glasses back, then were embittered and didn't give a damn. Thus we accumulated a dozen glasses and a bunch of forks. Leshka tied them all up neatly in his handkerchief with the evident intention of taking them along to his new home.

Grishka observed him suspiciously for a long time and finally expressed his opinion with conviction:

"Aha, you are lying! Told us you were "tried for a brawl." You're a thief, that's what. And you will be in a camp a hundred times, for certain!"

"Well! People live there too," Leshka objected idly.

DMITRII STREPETOV: our sixth companion, the most mature and serious. He is tall, with sharply cut features, stubborn black hair, and an obstinate strong-willed mouth. He is a worker from Orel, but his home town is Novosibirsk, and his parents still live there. He is twenty-two years old, finished seven grades, and has three specialities: chauffeur, tractor operator, and assistant locomotive engineer. Those are specialities! As we all saw when he

16

took out his wallet and showed us his certificate and licenses! He is needed everywhere and will find himself a place anywhere!

But by some irony of fate the train to Siberia worries Dimka Strepetov more than the rest of us. He imagines he won't find a place. I don't understand him, but suspect something is wrong—obviously something torments him. He stands at the window for hours and watches the kilometer posts pass by. He is depressed. Perhaps merely because it's so close here, nowhere to spread out, but is it necessary to go, and to go in a stuffy cage? Maybe because he is returning to his native area?

Dimka Strepetov more than the others is concerned for Vasek, and the latter becomes attached to him with all his heart. When Dmitrii is pensive, looking out the window, Vasek also looks beside him.

"Dim . . . does the bird-cherry tree grow in Siberia?"

"Where else?"

"I love the bird-cherry tree . . ."

And somehow it happened that whenever Dmitrii suggested something, everyone agreed, and when he ordered, everyone obeyed. Even the reliable and independent Ivan Bugai tacitly and amiably acknowledged his authority. But to Dimka this was not power; he simply led as an elder brother leads.

In departing from Moscow, we, being independent men, started to smoke at once, even Vasek, and it became obvious he had never smoked before. From our compartment emerged a cloud of smoke. Uncle Kostia, the conductor, came, placed his hands on his hips, and gazed at us with surprise for a moment. We sat silently and smoked.

"See here, generals," he said, appealing only to Dimka Strepetov, "I don't want to see this again. I appoint you head of the compartment."

"Aye, aye!" said Dimka, smiling.

When the conductor had left, he extinguished the cigarette butt with his heel.

"That's all, fellows. We'll go to the platform. Indeed, there are women and children here . . . And you, Vasek, are still too young; no need to squander cigarettes!"

After that we didn't smoke once in the car.

It's interesting to watch how Dimka and Vasek play chess. Vasek is sharp: a few quick moves and he has encircled his opponent, quickly and easily. But Dmitrii ponders the simplest of moves for a long time, thoughtfully frowns, and touches the chessmen with his clumsy fingers. Levers, steering wheels, rails—that's O.K., that suits him, but fragile finely-molded chessmen and the intricate game are not for him. He has lost many times, but doesn't give up and sits down to play again. Vasek is exceedingly pleased!

Dmitrii has no luck at cards either. A better partner for Leshka is not to be found in the whole world: Dimka naively believes everything and thinks only of his own combinations, never checking whether Leshka has beaten his ace by a trump or non-trump.

And so we, six different persons, travel in the same direction. And we are very good friends, and feel fine. We five friends (without Grigorii) go to the dining car, take the least expensive soup, and for the second course, tea, and we sit longer than anyone else. Passing through the "soft car," we disrespectfully slam the door and stamp our feet. At the stops we bargain longer than anyone with the peasant women, take berries and sunflower seeds by the handful to taste, and jump together on to the train when it has started. Uncle Kostia calls our compartment his guard.

Huts, sidings flash by, stars made out of stones at the mile-pillars, sometimes—a slogan hanging directly on the birches, something like "We are overtaking the USA in meat and milk production!" and hundreds of trackmen in clouds of dust raised by the train hold out yellow signal flags. We are going . . .

MISFORTUNE OR HAPPINESS?

I awoke because someone was shaking me:

"Tol, Tol', listen, wake up!"

18

Before me was the round, shining physiognomy of Leshka.

"What do you want?"

"Do you have any money?"

"What is it?"

"Don't keep it in your trousers. Someone is sneaking about. I noticed him some time ago. Count your money if you wish and give it to me. He won't take it from me . . . Don't trust me? As you wish . . . Then hide it beneath your undershirt. Like that. I'll watch out."

"Listen, Leshka, is it the one who cut off Ivan's watch?"

"No."

"No?"

"No, not him. Someone else. I know, but I can't say. Sleep."

He dived below and plummeted to his berth like a sack. I tried to sleep but couldn't—it was stuffy.

The car swayed; the ceiling bulb burned at one-quarter capacity; there was the bad odor of socks and feet—these feet of various sizes protrude from each berth, bare or in socks full of holes from which the toes stick out; on one berth two pair of feet, one large, male, and the other, female, in stockings. Grandmas and children sleep side by side on their bundles. It is stuffy and dim.

I got off my berth and went to the platform. Opened the door—and felt dizzy. The wheels clattered, swift dim shadows flashed by. It was raining, and the handrails were wet; large drops splattered; lightning suddenly flashed and illuminated for a moment the pillars, boulders, flattened grass, and low ragged clouds. The air was improbably fresh, smelt of pine-tree resin and ozone.

The car shook, swerved, the train going at frenetic speed.

I leaned out forward and almost suffocated from the wind. I only noticed our long train with an electric-powered locomotive ahead bending on the curve. We almost always travel with an electric locomotive. In Europe their steam locomotives still puff, but here—beautiful, smokeless, and powerful machines.

I don't remember when it happened, when it came, but today Siberia is here.

19

An endless country . . . One can learn in school the statistics of its frontiers, measure on the map the thousands of kilometers from Kaliningrad to the Bering Strait, but, truly, unless you cross it yourself in this way, you won't comprehend, nor feel, its vastness. We travel, and travel, and travel, the train had already become our home, our hands and feet have pins and needles, and we staggered when getting out at stops. The fields, forests, logs, plains. still not half-way to the Pacific Ocean. The stations here are far away from one another, and plains or ordinary forests stretch out everywhere. This is territory like anywhere else, only vaster, sparsely settled, almost untouched.

I look into the darkness, my eyes are still unaccustomed to it: no light, nor glow. A vast, unimaginable land extends, breathes, blooms, teems with wild life and birds, sparkles with deposits and lakes—and it waits. Perhaps we are right to go to Siberia? Maybe this is not a misfortune, but happiness.

I don't know anything, only I'm not myself. Today for the first time I have felt Siberia.

LIGHTS OF A LARGE CITY

First, the sky became brighter in the distance. Then a bright spot appeared. And suddenly, unexpectedly, fairy-tale lights were sprinkled about. The train rattled, speeding on, but they rained down all round, and the entire ground was covered with them. Uncle Kostia, yawning, went out and started to wipe off the handrails, lit the lantern, and popped out the door.

Then came Dimka Strepetov. He was disheveled and out of character. He was excited. We were approaching Novosibirsk.

"Are you going into the city with me?" he asked. "You don't know what city this is. Gosh, you don't know anything!"

We jumped down to the platform end, through an underground passage, ran to the station. I was blinded by the chandeliers, marble, and plate-glass windows. I must admit that never in my life had I seen such a palace. Here everything was convenient, everything was at hand, beautiful, and cozy. Despite the late hour, all kiosks, the restaurant, and the barber were open."

"We have the most beautiful station in the Union," muttered Dimka. "Let's go, Let's go!"

We ran into the square and walked along the pavement. It was spacious, peaceful, and fresh. There was a smell of pinks from the flower-beds. Windows were lighted somewhere in the large houses on the other side of the square. You felt like strolling, straight ahead, well-proportioned and beautiful.

"My grandma lives over there," Dimka pointed excitedly. "I was so muddle-headed, I should have sent a telegram so she would meet us! . . . My sister lives there, just nearby, a ten-minute walk. Aha!. . ."

"Listen! let's take a taxi," I suggested. "The train stops for fifty minutes. We'll make it!"

"By taxi? He looked me in the eyes with fear.—"Never. You don't understand . . . Say, this is a beautiful city, beautiful, isn't it? Say! This is Siberia! Understand? Say it? Isn't it?"

Well, I don't know how to express delight aloud. Beautiful. Yes, very! And we stood silently in the square. Dimka worried, but I looked, listened, and inhaled the smell of pinks.

Why didn't he want to take a taxi? That I didn't understand. I hadn't gotten to know Dimka. He dragged me to the station, then stopped, looked about, and again ran on.

We returned to our stuffy car. There Dimka grabbed his rucksack and darted toward the exit. I barely caught up and grabbed the flap.

"Where to?"

"I'm getting off!"

"You're crazy! And the contract?"

"Let them search for me. While they try to find me, I'll earn money—repay the travel expenses. Let me go!"

"Dimka, what's with you?"

"Let go!"

"Sit down. Calm down. Why are you going? What have you been thinking? Work at the construction site, then return. Don't lose your senses!"

He sat down, dropping the rucksack and gazed out one window, then another. The train was still standing. The speaker announced: "Departing in five minutes . . . Visitors, check to see you haven't kept the tickets of those leaving . . ." Dimka must be held for these five minutes. I held. I don't recall what I said, and he didn't even listen. Finally, the train moved on, and again the lights poured down. Little by little they thinned out, disappeared, and darkness stretched out.

Possibly Dimka's sadness and emotion were to blame, but I thought of Novosibirsk with a feeling of excitement, as something beautiful and fairytale-like.

"Well, why did you want to get off?"

"Don't you know where we're going? Even a bear might die there . . ."

"You're afraid?"

"You wait, you yourself will want to escape ten times over and won't be able to. Yes, I'm afraid! So what?"

Could that be Dimka Strepetov? Our stern, mature, obstinate commander? I couldn't believe his words.

"Listen, Dimka, you're talking nonsense."

"Yes, nonsense! And don't ask anything more. But Novosibirsk is better than Leningrad, better than Moscow! Someday all Siberia will be like that, you understand! At Taiga Station I have a friend. I'm getting off there and I shall return. I shall come back!"

Dima had spoken "nonsense," but all the same I didn't feel so well.

I didn't understand anything.

The wheels clattered. Carelessly sprawled out, Fat Leshka slept clothed, and his chromium boots bumped against our knees every minute. Clasping his bundles, Greedy Grigorii turned peacefully. Ivan Bugai raised himself, gazed at us uncomprehendingly and then muttered: "Shut up, you inconsiderate slobs"—scratched himself, and snored again the sleep of a righteous and upright fellow.

22

And we sat and discussed: must one master oneself or not? I was not firmly convinced this was necessary but considered it my duty to "hold" Dimka. He told me of his life, how he had worked on a locomotive and nearly gone through a red light, and then served in the Army. After the Army, he had returned to Novosibirsk and fallen in love with a lady geologist.

"What did I know then? What could I tell her? About the locomotive? About the machine gun, the breech-block, the sight?"

"And then?"

"I worked again on a locomotive, was constantly on trips, all covered with soot, but she loved me. And she often went on expeditions . . . Why had we married? She always was in the taiga; I couldn't stand that taiga! There is no human life there, like nomads. Then we moved to Orel and separated. Her people to Siberia, but I raked her up in my arms and, on the contrary, we went further away from Siberia. I worked as a driver, had an apartment. It didn't work out. Finally, we separated, and the matter ended. She again went to the taiga, and I was recruited . . ."

Morning came, but we talked on. We passed through the beautiful and austere Taiga Station, where the air was fresh and resinous, just as after a thunderstorm.

Dimka hadn't gotten off.

VASEK LEARNS ABOUT LIFE

In the afternoon our Fat Leshka and Vasek went to the dining car. Vasek returned alone two hours later. He was completely drunk, bumped his head against the berths, and hiccupped. True he didn't come back independently: an inspector led him in and asked in every compartment:

"Is this yours?"

We gasped with surprise. Soft-hearted women began to rummage and chuck:

23

"Oh, such a young man, still a child! Shame on you, are you not ashamed, good-for-nothings, to bring this lad to this!"

Vasek obscenely and clumsily swore and asked to smoke. Grisha shrank back with disgust and climbed up to his berth.

"His pockets are turned inside out, they robbed him!" he whispered with terror, sticking out his finger with a large black nail.

"Let's go and punch Leshka on the nose," said Bugai tersely; he snorted and his nostrils dilated.

Vasek moaned and trembled. Under the gaze of the entire car we three led him to the washroom, poured cold water on his head, and then lay him down on Dimka's kit-bag. Bugai and Strepetov went to the dining car to punch Leshka on the nose, and I stayed to care for Vasek because he raged and struck his head on the small table. Soon he vomited against the wall and on Dimka's bag. Uncle Kostia rushed in, grabbed his head, began to swear and to curse us violently.

I again took Vasek to the washroom. Finally he became better and slept. I looked through his pockets, the seventy rubles had gone.

Then Uncle Kostia silently beckoned me to his compartment:

"Well? Haven't I cleaned up after him?" he said. "Now we'll draw up a document 'On bringing the passenger car of a train into an unsanitary state'."

He said this solemnly, relishing such an imposing definition.

I felt confused. Uncle Kostia quietly began to scratch something down on a paper.

"Well, now, close the door. Let's not raise any noise, generals. I have seen nothing, and whoever has, it's none of his business. Give me some dough and get lost. Well?"

Blushing, I almost mechanically gave him fifteen rubles and left, feeling as if a bucket of cold water had been poured over me. Take that Uncle Kostia! . . .

The last straw would be if Bugai and Strepetov were arrested for the brawl in the dining car and put off the train. I rushed to the dining car, already having pictured in my mind broken glassware, clattering dishes, and over-turned tables.

Surprisingly, the dining car was quiet. Around a table in the corner sat the smiling, radiant Leshka, my remarkable Dimka Strepetov and Ivan Bugai, drinking . . . together.

Opposite them, on the edge of a chair, a character sat watchfully in an open shirt with awesome tattoos on his arms: a grave, cross, pistol, anchor, and the inscription: "I shall never forget my true mother." The following conversation ensued among those seated:

"You scoundrel, did you sneak off with the watch?"

"No, not me."

"You lie!"

"Not me, I tell you!"

"But you are a sneak thief?"

"Yes. A sneak thief."

"I find it interesting. What of it?"

"Then tell us about your life."

"Not without a drink. Stand me to 500 grams and I'll tell you."

They began to bargain and settled on 150. Each contributed three rubles and they ordered vodka in concert for their interlocutor and beer for themselves. Six hands grabbed me and so politely seated me that the table toppled. I called them, dragged them, and barely escaped myself.

With heavy heart I returned to the sleeping Vas'ka, and the lads remained to hear about the petty thief's life. They returned later when the dining car closed and they were thrown out. Bugai was relatively sober.

"Well, what has your companion told you?"

"Oh, Tol'ka, don't be malicious. Rubbish, oh what rubbish!"

"What's rubbish?"

"Everything is rubbish. Dull!"

"Then why did you sit there?"

"We had to extract Vasek's money."

"Did you get it?"

"Yes."

"Where is it?"

"We drank it up."

He plonked himself down on his jacket and for a long time didn't sleep; he lay there staring at the ceiling and was thinking of something long and arduous, like our trip. Again feet of various sizes protrude from the berths. Now the difference from Moscow time is five hours. At the Bolshoi Theater a performance is beginning now: a crowd of people on business trips seethes and fishes for tickets. And for me there is no return, and no return for Dimka to Novosibirsk or to Taiga Station.

I haven't said where we are going. We are travelling to the Bratsk Hydroelectric Power Station.

WHAT'S SWEETER: HORSERADISH OR RADISH?

In the morning the lads pooled their money, some contributing 10 and others two rubles, and slipped it into Vas'ka's jacket while he slept. But after what had happened yesterday, Vasek had a headache; he got up bored, confused, and depressed. Dima Strepetov again went to the platform and stood there at the open door for a whole hour. Bugai, angry, restless, got out part three of a Physics textbook, turned the powerful back of his head, and forced himself to read. Only Leshka, the kid, smiled as though nothing had happened; he lay about, paunch upwards, and hummed a song which has never been recorded, a song of another world. I had nothing to do, so I lay on the third berth and unhurriedly took down the words:

. . . I was born on the Volga, in a fisherman's family.

Of the family not a trace remains.

Although mother loved me so dearly,

Mine was one hell of a fate.

26

In those days I hated to work,
Neither to mow, nor to plough, nor to be a tailor,
But together with gay chaps called ruffians,
Learned to tramp about the world.
We loved one another very strongly then,
Although for the first time we met timidly,
But one night they invited me,
To be at a very risky affair.
Oh, the night was as though one's eyes had been put out!
But a thief bears the risk, as usual.
We worked there, well for not more than an hour.
And, like wolves, returned with the spoils.
. . . The violin sang a free Danube tune,
And an accordion poured forth . . .

"The little bag! The little bag! Where's my little bag?"

We all started at this hysterical outcry. Grishka, perplexed, pale, began to toss on his berth. Then he suddenly rolled head over heels from there and seized Leshka by the neck.

"Scum, thief, give it back! Give it back, I say! Give back the money!"

A racket kicked up in our compartment. The curious already were staring in from the aisle.

"I'll cut you to pieces, I'll cut you to pieces! Give it back . . ."

"You get lost!" said Leshka, proudly pushing him away. "What are you to me, nit."

"Give it back, I say, give it back; I'll call the conductor! You traced it, you knew!"

With Ivan's help we separated them into corners and accepted the case for examination. In the morning the little bag with the money was still in its place. In it, as Grigorii asserted, was about 1,500 rubles. One couldn't stand to look at him: he trembles, sobs, unbuttons his trousers, and shows the remnants of string. Leshka is surprised and knits his brow.

"I wouldn't dirty my hands with you! You kulak, you marmot, you stinking polecat! Well, go find your bag!"

"Thief! Convict! Ah, ah . . ."

For fifteen minutes there is an exchange of epithets. Grishka howls and cries out at them, choking. Leshka laughs with contempt. Ivan Bugai undertook to search for the little bag. They ransacked Grishka's berth, turned all his bundles inside out, and looked on the other berths. The little bag was found behind a pipe under the table. Evidently at night it had torn away, and when Grigorii sat at the table to eat breakfast it had slipped down and behind.

Grishka, trembling, grabbed it, climbed to his berth, and remained quiet for a long time. Leshka continued his song. But I did not continue to write down the words; I was disturbed and thought: why were they so, Grishka and Leshka, and whence have they come? And which of them is better? In books, newspapers, and journals I hardly ever encountered them. There they had emerged most recently in the 1920s. And here they are, side by side with me; they eat, they sleep, they swear . . .

Were I to be transformed into Grishka, I would—word of honor—hang myself! What is this anyhow? How many more generations are necessary for the kulak in man to die?

And Leshka? And the character who found it "so interesting" to be a petty thief? Each has his own world, his own morality, his own "folklore," and contempt for those who are not like them . . .

Leshka, of course, despises Grigorii, but is horseradish sweeter than radish?

WE SHALL SORT OUT THE GINGERBREAD

Taishet! Taishet!

This word is on everyone's tongue. From Taishet Station begins the new railway to the Lena. Soon the entire world will hear of it, but at the moment it is known only to a few. It extends across the Lena to Irkutsk, through mountain ranges and untamed lands to Chukotka, to the Bering Strait itself. We now travel to Bratsk along the first segment.

I knew about this route from the map, but since I still had 300 rubles I had bought a ticket to Irkutsk. Instead of transferring at Taishet I decided to travel the old route: to Iakutsk and from there by steamship along the Angara. That is so interesting!

My fellow travellers get off at Taishet to wait for the Bratsk train, and I . . . travel farther. Perhaps I should get off with them? No. We'll meet at the Bratsk Hydroelectric Power Station within a week. We write down one another's names and nothing more. They have no addresses, nor have I.

From sunrise on it rains. Here there is expanse and sweep to everything: a trip, until you are stupefied; forest, it is boundless; rain, constantly without brightening. It pours and pours, streaming along the windows; dampness and cold have even penetrated into our overcrowded car.

Soon Taishet, any moment it will come into sight. The authorized agent who accompanies the party of recruits came by and ordered them to make ready. Grishka grumbles so that they help him carry his belongings. The lads are noticeably absorbed and anxious.

"Gosh, we'll arrive and there will only be tents standing!" says Vasek.

"Never mind, Vasek," smiled Dmitrii, "we'll have to pitch them ourselves."

"The agent said we'll work in timber-processing. There's something."

"Oh, they will make us carry logs," muttered Grishka, "with our eyes bulging . . . !"

"No, we'll sort out gingerbread. In a pastry factory."

Tiny houses and smoking chimneys already were to be seen.

"Taishet! What kind of factory is that!"

"No doubt it's our pastry factory. Let's go, lads!"

29

We shake hands with one another. My farewell to Dimka Strepetov for some reason felt sorrowful.

Many people got off the train. They all looked like migrants: kids, dishes, provisions. The rain lashes, the mud is impassable, the train is soaked, confusion, and the station is not in sight. The agent shouts and verifies the list to see whether everyone has gotten off.

Then they hoisted their trunks, suitcases, and bundles on their shoulders and went somewhere along the track, through puddles, jumping over the sleepers. And with all the others went the restless Dmitrii, the thorough Ivan Bugai, the lazy thief Leshka, and greedy Grigorii, and Vasek who knows life—to build the Bratsk Hydroelectric Power Station.

Only Dmitrii turned and waved to me. The others already were engaged with various concerns: whether they would succeed in hiding from the rain, whether Grishka's junk would be dragged safely, and perhaps they were simply anxious and afraid.

End of the First Notebook

THE DISCOVERY OF AMERICA

The great enemy of man is: fear. Fear of change in life. To a person who has sat in one place for twenty years it is terrifying to move somewhere else, to go to a neighboring area or—God save us!—to Siberia.

Having tried this myself, I began to understand a bit. I didn't sit in my home town for twenty years, and I had studied in school for only ten years. And suddenly changes in life! How terrifying it was to go somewhere else! To leave home, travel among alien people, to strange parts? What will I do? How will I live?

Most likely I had left with eyes narrowed. I recognize only myself. Because we don't admit we are afraid. Young people travelling to Siberia look to be in very good spirits, speak various fine phrases at meetings. But I say: terrifying.

Now I'm almost not afraid. Vasek taught me not to be afraid, a carefree petty thief—without money or belongings—who travelled together with everyone and didn't lay his head down for long: but how will I live, and all of a sudden will it be bad? Dmitrii Strepetov and Ivan Bugai taught me not to be afraid, who if it is difficult will make jokes at the expense of gingerbread and, out of the blue, pitch a tent.

Now that frightened and confused lad who a week ago cried: "What is to be done? What will be? To the factory, to the fuel dump!" seems odd to me.

It seems to me that I've grown up in several days.

And if Vic fails the examination for university I shall advise him to travel to Siberia in an ordinary car on the third berth. Baggage, Vic, don't bring, you need nothing except a change of underwear and a bar of good soap.

I say this in complete seriousness, hear?

And don't be afraid!

THE SECOND NOTEBOOK

THREE STARS

There are many textbooks in the world.

We study mountains, seas, and minerals. They taught us that the sum of the squares of two sides is equal to the square of the hypotenuse. I know how alternating current is transformed into direct current, and I read in the textbook about the reaction of "iron plus H_2SO_4."

But where can one buy a textbook of life?

We had a wonderful literature teacher, Nadezhda Vasil'evna. She told us ardently about the ideological orientation of *Evgenii Onegin,* about class struggle in Gorky's tale *Mother* and in Sholokhov's *Opening the Virgin Lands,* and everything under those conditions, in the life of those times, was so clear, comprehensible, and shelved in order.

But our days, the life of today? The teachers were concerned to get through Onegin and Pechorin within the allocated hours, and the curriculum plan provided not even a minute for a talk about life. As though how modern man should be in our day is evident to everyone, nothing more is to be said! But take Sashka and Vic—each of them understands this in his own way! People become enemies without even having finished school, although each diligently studied both Onegin and Pechorin and *Opening the Virgin Lands*.

Raising his glass at the graduation evening, the Director said: "Now you are entering life. Live up to the name of Soviet Man so that our school may be proud of you!"

We understandably all to a man promised to be worthy. Sincerely, warmly! And certainly at all graduation evenings in all schools everyone promises to be worthy of the same Soviet Man. Strange, then, whence these scoundrels come?

Perhaps hot arguments and conversations openly about us and about life in which we speak should take place in the Komsomol committee? I don't know about other schools, but in ours the Komsomol organizer decided with the committee such basic matters as membership dues and skiing contests. There was one meeting during the entire time "On the Moral Aspect of Soviet Man," but it was uninteresting; they read dull reports from notes, and in the cloakroom they wouldn't give back coats so that no one would leave. This resembled more an obligation, and it is doubtful whether anyone wanted to think about the moral aspect except to fill in the plan: "measure" has been carried out . . . I don't even recall what was said in the reports—it seems to me examples were cited from books and that Pavel Korchagin and Maras'ev were remembered.

Once, while a bit tight, Vic's father spoke about life:

"Modern life, young people, is a wilderness teeming with vermin. He who is the first to bite the other's throat, he is right. Beautiful ideas are to be found only in books, they are for external use."

Yes, we avidly read *How Steel Was Tempered* and *Two Captains*. These are books of other periods. Were we to live with Pavel Korchagin we would fight the Whites. Oh, how we would have fought! Were we to live with Oleg Koshev, we would have defeated the Fascists. But now? Who refutes Vic's father? Mother told me:

"All so long as we are young yearn to go somewhere, to seek the truth, but later we get used to it . . . The best thing to do: find yourself a quiet corner and live modestly, peacefully. God is with them, with rank and money. Life is so cruel, don't climb, don't seek justice. You won't find it!"

Now she thinks I'm missing and weeps day and night.

We were enthusiastic about the Virgin Lands together with everyone else (they smelled of Korchagin, of a tempestuous life!). Then Vic's father (with "the wisdom of life") explained to us that only fools go to the Virgin Lands, that they entice us to forced labor, so we cooled off at once and were even ready to complain about the Virginlanders. Vic's father never refused to explain life to us.

"My dear ones," he said laughing, "look about you: business-like people don't give a damn for your Korchagin. It is you while young who amuse yourselves, read various books, and get excited, but people are concerned about money, an overcoat, an apartment; those who are smarter or more cunning advance—look, already ride in their own car. Sharpen your teeth, the teeth!"

Finally Vic appeared at school elegantly dressed, in slim trousers, shoes with buckles and thick soles, and declared that to live without misfortune, without want, happily: that is the wisdom of life because life is short and youth even shorter.

The Komsomol organizer said to him: "Ah, you are a *stiliaga!*"* But Vic objected and proved that "style" is useful and good. Even Chekhov said that people should dress beautifully; slim trousers don't hang loosely on one's feet, like skirts, and don't fray, and thick soles are useful in mud. This was absolutely correct. I myself would have dressed in style if my mother had earned as much as Vic's father.

But to do this one must cut throats—mustn't one? I don't want to! I don't want to! I don't want them to be right!

And are they right?

Where, oh where, is a textbook about life to be found? Not a statute nor

---

* (Soviet youth in the late 1950s who preferred Western styles of dress, music, and the like—transl.)

a Digest of laws, but an ordinary intelligent and honest dialogue, a dialogue about souls, how to live life now, how to live ardently and honestly?

Our dear School Director, our esteemed mentors! You imparted to us a mass of useful things, you gave us knowledge. Thank you! But you yourselves have certainly not noticed that you have passed over in silence something so great, so important. You have thoughtfully created a rosy legend about the easy life awaiting us, that for the young the road is everywhere, as though it merely remains for us to sit in an easy chair, mouth open, and swallow the blessings given to us on a plate—and released us into the world: "be worthy," that is, pull yourself through.

And how does one pull oneself through?

AN ANCIENT EGYPTIAN STREETCAR

"One can work in Siberia for a year, a year and a half, and earn a lot of money. Then I can dress decently, will want for nothing, stand on my feet, and there—we can but see—buy a car and return to Moscow. How will Iuna look at me then? Vic, of course, will gasp . . . And, after all, life is short, and youth even shorter. What if in fact this is the wisest thing to do? The wisest thing . . ."

These thoughts climbed into my head when I, left alone, lay silently on my berth for the entire segment from Taishet to Irkutsk.

The "Volga"—an astounding automobile! You sit somewhat nonchalantly behind the wheel. Your car awaits you at the theater, and you leave the theater with a girl and say to her: "Please." The door clicks—and the asphalt strip speeds below the radiator. "Is it true that life is difficult in Siberia?" asks Iuna. "Of course, it's not easy. Courageous men are needed there. Siberia—is the modern Klondike . . ."

Why, if a person is alone, is he so helpless? Why is he so weak? To achieve something in life one must go such a long way, one must knock about among strangers, people engaged in their own affairs and indifferent to you!

36

I got off on the Irkutsk platform and my cheerfulness began to wane, to wane . . .

I was confused in the noisy crowd and couldn't find the exit to the city. Everyone around me was in a hurry, ran. They shouted in your ears: "Hot pirozhki! Fresh hot borshch!" Conversations, flowers, kisses, laughter. Everyone is being welcomed, everyone is going somewhere, they have their homes, family, or acquaintances. And I all of a sudden felt so alone, unwanted by anyone. A person simply hangs about in the world somehow. For what does he hang about? Why?

The pier turned out to be not far from the station, beyond the bridge. From the bridge the Angara was majestic, wide, with surprisingly rapid and beautiful waters. Cutters, boats sailed, and a tugboat spluttered, swinging a barge about.

The deserted landing-stage smelled of hot planks, resinous and slimy. At the ticket office I read the time-table. There were no boats to Bratsk today.

I wanted to look about, to feel whether I was not out of place! I was on edge, anxious: the time-table had completely unsettled me. I sat on an over-turned boat, watched how the women laundered linen in the river, and in order to calm myself, began to convince and remind myself that everything was fine!

First, I am still en route, still not at the Bratsk Hydroelectric Power Station. I am a passenger, a tourist. I still have 300 rubles. Second, it is even better that there is no boat. One ought to see the city, and below the city the Irkutsk Hydroelectric Power Station is being built—this too one must see.

And I will spend the night on the shore, even if under this boat. The world on the whole is beautiful, and nothing therein passes unnoticed. Beyond your nose, Tolia! I washed myself in Angara water, cold as ice, drying myself with a hankie, picked up my little suitcase, and proceeded at random about Irkutsk with mixed thoughts.

Well, hello Siberia. I have arrived.

This it turns out is an amazing, incomparable feeling—when one arrives in an unfamiliar city and comes to know it, one discovers in it something characteristic and unique.

For the first time in my life I saw wooden sidewalks. They are rows of planks laid along both sides of the streets, clean, polished by many feet; to walk along them is pleasant and rather peaceful and comfortable: clop-clop . . .

The streets of Irkutsk were quiet, shady, and from morning on, hot and dusty, as though this were not Siberia, but Central Asia. The city smelled of summer, dust and hot foliage. Passers-by did not hurry, didn't rush as they did along the Okhotnyi Row; dress was simple and modest—and everyone seemed to be cordial. Automobiles were rare; the drivers drove carefully and sounded their horns a hundred paces from the crosswalk. In Moscow we are completely out of the habit of honking.

On dusty fences are seen the frightening jaws of lions, and the advertisement cried out as it can only do, to be sure, in the provinces:

THREE!!! LAST PERFORMANCES! THREE!!!
A MIXED GROUP OF BEASTS OF PREY
UNDER THE MANAGEMENT OF N. GLADIL'SHCHIKOV!
FIVE CLOWNS IN THE RING!
AN EVENING OF SHEER LAUGHTER!
COME IN TO LAUGH!

"Grandma, can you show me how to get into the center of town?"

"To the center, son? Take the streetcar."

"What streetcar?"

"Number one, son."

I went to the stop and began to wait for number one. Streetcars came, but . . . they always were without numbers. "How strange,"—I thought—"how do people distinguish them?" The unnumbered streetcars crept up frequently, nobody announced anything, but the passengers got on, somehow guessing the wanted streetcar. The crowd at the stop was large, people rushed

38

to work, and the doors of the cars engaged in battle. A morose tall old man with a chair could not make it even into the third streetcar. I asked him timidly.

"Tell me, please, what number is this?"

"None."

"How's that?"

"Aha, you are from the station? In Irkutsk there is one line. Understand?"

One! To hell with them! In ancient Egypt to be sure the streetcars were better. Aha-a!

The next streetcar crept up to the stop, and the strange old man dashed to the steps. I followed him so successfully that the crowd lifted me off the ground and literally carried me through the door.

Imagine such a squat red structure similar to an enlarged matchbox with a tiny pitiful light in front which jingles a mournful "ding-dong"; it drones, rolls, and within is so packed with people that one can neither breathe nor budge; only the roof creaks. The heroic conductor gives signals with the aid of a cord and shouts:

"Fares! Get ready to get off!"

The line was a very long one; it extended throughout the entire city. I got off where most of the people did, that is, they carried me out again. In a glass case hung the *East-Siberian Pravda*, and there I read, by the way, that in the near future "Irkutsk will be embellished by a trolley bus." A page of the newspaper was devoted to the young builders of the television center. "In a world of miracles" the note about television was called. It was so astonishing to me: here this was still a miracle of the future. And suddenly, I clearly experienced, understood, for the first time—how many things there were in the country and how many cities there still are without streetcars, and everything to which one had been long accustomed in Moscow. A streetcar is a trifle, it simply led one to stumble across these thoughts, and I stopped with surprise and looked about with different eyes . . .

The usual street life flowed by, but to me everything seemed new, special. I wanted to understand this unfamiliar city and its people. They live far away in Siberia—by what do they live? Where are they going? Do they all have worries or do they simply stroll? Ice cream on the corners; a crush at the kiosks selling flavored waters; fish tails wiggle in an old women's bag—strange fish I recall that I had seen in pictures. A sterlet! Along the roadway travels a cabman unhurriedly, a real live cabman. A pretty good bookstore, still locked up; but in the window *Martin Iden*; in Moscow this was unavailable . . . Dusty, dilapidated "Pobeda" taxis; there are no "walk" signs, cross wherever you like.

Houses—there are various types, each one alive and with its own character. There are no flat monumental rows of façades. The houses probably were built at various times, in different styles, the intervals between them filled in by small pavilions, ivy, and all in all are something very warm and cozy. Each street is like a book shelf in a library. There stand brand-new volumes smelling of paint with crisp pages—and side by side some pamphlet or some respected glued-together *Monte Cristo* outliving its era.

There are enormous new dwelling houses, an ancient theater and the majestic colonnaded Administration of the Eastern Siberian Railway. And if one turned into a side-street, timber-framed houses of thick logs were crowded together with dark-brown, white-shuttered little houses, with gates from the same thick logs and signs: "Vicious dogs in the yard." It seemed to me that I had fallen into the world of an Ostrovskii play. And all of a sudden immediately alongside is a modern, noisy, asphalt yard with a children's playground and a volleyball court—just like Moscow. Only in front of a fresh new building, in the yard, blocked up with lime barrels and various boards, there still stuck out a squat merchant's warehouse with rusty corrugated blinds, an ancient lock, and a modern sign "Univermag".*

It seemed that the houses were wrestling with one another. Old and small ones, blackened, with vicious dogs wanted to sit quietly in their peaceful corners; they raised cabbage and carried it to the bazaar. But the new, gay ones

* (Department Store—transl.)

stood out; they stood where they were wanted—young, confident, not always noticing how with wolf-like malevolence the bent iron blinds gnash the warehouse, how the timber frames hasten away with the throng, in bushes, under foliage, angrily flash their bloated tiny windows: their quiet has been disturbed, how terrible!

A BRILLIANT BOOTBLACK

Wandering about, I stumbled upon a bootblack. He was situated near a stone fence in a cozy shaded spot. Along the fence, silent and unseen, sat several fat lazy men who examined passers-by and from time to time conversed with one another. My boots were dusty and had almost worn white. I hesitantly stopped.

The bootblack silently, with the motion of a conjurer, threw a stool to me. I sat down, and the fat ones began to inspect me from head to toe.

I don't know where and by whom he had been taught, but such virtuosity, such a wondrous bootblack, I had never encountered. His hands flashed so rapidly that they seemed to have dissolved in the air; one heard only the sound of the brushes, like the hum of an electric fan. The bootblack's small brushes and boxes, bootblack-balls, pebbles, rags were merely glimpsed. He had five or six sorts of brushes. He tossed a brush with his right hand, grabbed a small box, meanwhile caught the brush with his left hand, sent it under his knee, and a velvet ribbon already flew in the air . . .

I simply became numb, and the fat ones watched carpingly, with the air of experts and connoisseurs. I understood that this was a bootblack of talent, a bootblack-celebrity, and around him, just as around an artist, gather admirers and supporters. From time to time someone sighed excitedly and egged him on:

"Go, Sergei, go!"

Under the tornado of brushes I was a victim, a guinea-pig, a conjurer's

41

assistant. From time to time Sergei by unknown means extracted from his box a long chatterbox-roulade: "Trr-r-ra, Trr–to!"—this meant: change your feet.

The shine lasted for an unbearably long time; I perspired and forgot about everything in the world. My old, worn-out boots began to shine like a mirror; the cracks and creases disappeared; the sun was reflected in the boots, and a few passing clouds.

Finally, a prolonged, especially intricate roulade having been heard, Sergei straightened up with an expressionless face.

I felt as one does after a storm.

"How much?"

Sergei was silent. There was a moment of anxious tension.

"A r-ruble," said one fat man.

"Two," whispered another.

I gave three.

I walked away, casting a sidelong look at my boots, and suddenly felt happy. Why, I don't understand, but it was as though someone pressed my elbow and whispered: "Don't worry, everything is fine!"

It was as though yet another very major issue had been resolved that had long troubled me. What problem?

In reality nothing had happened. Simply I was en route to the Irkutsk Hydroelectric Power Station in shined boots. Sometimes I remembered the silent, brilliant master, Sergei, smiled, and just shook my head . . .

A TAINTED BAIKAL SALMON

"Well, and if I punch you on the nose?" he asked in quiet fury.

I also had come to hate him, but looked up and simply understood that if he struck me, there would be nothing left: from his blue tennis shirt protruded not hands but solid knots of muscles.

He was dark-complexioned, powerful, crew-cut, and looked like a boxer.

42

On the bends the crowd fell against me, I toppled against him, and he quietly supported everyone, only the knots on his hands swelled slightly.

"What am I doing? They are pushing me."

"But if I punch you on the nose?" he repeated his question, staring point-blank and flexing his muscles.

The bus to the Irkutsk Hydroelectric Power Station is an entire epic. Ragged, with broken doors, the windows boarded up with plywood, packed to the limit, it flew downhill like a barrel of herrings, bounced, banged, raised dust. You couldn't make out anything, and sweat poured into your eyes. The bus flew past the stops by a hundred meters, one or two passengers got off, and the first of the waiting ran to the rear door; this miracle of transport roared, joyfully poured exhaust on them, and left them swearing to their heart's content and spitting in clouds of smoke.

"Fares! Anyone getting off at the crossing? No? Driver, don't open the door!"

After the next spurt, when I was flattened against my enemy in the blue tennis shirt so that I almost crushed my nose on his hard chest, my neighbor hissed and carefully moved his foot. And only then did I understand with terror that for a quarter-hour I had been standing with my heel on his toes.

"Excuse me, I'm sorry, I didn't know!"

Instead of an answer he raised his enormous fist, smacking of iron, to my nose and suddenly turned to another neighbor:

"Well, is it any good to you? A naive one, he pinched my work orders. Give them back."

A stupefied lad of fifteen years, clad only in a jacket on his naked body, without a word put out his hand and extended a pack of crumpled pink papers. My enemy in the tennis shirt quietly took them and thrust them into his bosom. I understood nothing.

"Kuz'mikha. Anyone getting off? No?"

"Oh, let me through! Oh, people!"

"Why didn't you say so? Stop the bus! Hey, hey. Knock!"

"Let the old woman through. Let go of her sack!"

43

"Wait, wait a minute! Oh, Lord!"

"Go on. Driver, go on!"

What a journey. My heart stopped, and I couldn't breathe. At a steep turn everyone was knocked about for the last time, and the conductor announced: "First settlement. We have arrived," but I couldn't collect myself, got off, staggering, on to the pavement, and felt creepy all over.

The construction site was beyond the city, far up the Angara. A pleasant breeze blew. A spotless unusual little town, asphalt streets, lawns, cheerful pink or blue two-story houses with bi-colored slate roofs in a chessboard pattern. The street names were unusual: Borodin, Mukhina, Iakobi, Theater, Maritime Province . . . And then the construction site!

There it is, the famous Siberian construction site! Crane towers stick out from afar, conveyors buzz—the settlement is still being built . . . And here a fire engine stands in the middle of the street, and helmeted firemen with hatchets busily wash rubbish into the gutters and water the lawns. A skewbald cow wanders along the asphalt. On a plaque is the announcement: "Today in the First Settlement Club: "Dreams on the Highways.""

I hadn't eaten since morning and therefore, having seen a sign "Canteen," decided: I'll have breakfast and then move on to the construction site.

It was noisy and hot in the canteen, and there was a purely "canteen" aroma of fried meat and dirty dishes; some pitiful palm trees stood at the windows. At each table there were five or ten beer glasses, so there was no room for plates. Chat, loud laughter, smoke. A queue at the cashier.

I had just reached the cashier's window when suddenly someone tugged my sleeve. I turned around—my "enemy" in the blue tennis shirt shoved a tenner to me:

"Take it and buy me what you get."

"O.K. . . . I still don't know . . ."

"Cabbage soup with pork, Baikal salmon, and stewed fruit. Tainted salmon—there! Will you have it?"

"Let's."

At the table he smiled good-naturedly and extended a broad hard palm:

44

"Leonid. You have plagued me for no reason. Almost clobbered you. My toes still hurt: a brick fell on my foot . . . I see you're not local?"

"From Moscow."

"Hm-m. I'm a Siberian. A native one . . . Going to work here?"

"No, just looking about. I'm travelling to the Bratsk Hydroelectric Power Station."

"There's nothing to do here? Hold it! You've hardly eaten your salmon! Now you'll try it. I've been here since the first day . . . Oh, you traveller! . . ."

The last remark did not relate to me. At the adjacent table, sprawled out, sat our neighbor on the bus, the lad in the jacket. He asked the waitress for two glasses of hot water, extracted a tiny onion from his pocket, cut it, salted it thickly, took bread from the bowl, spread mustard on it, and started to tuck into this strange breakfast, drinking only hot water with it.

Leonid suddenly leapt up, thrust money to someone again at the cashier, got hold of the waitress—otherwise we would have surely waited a whole hour—and on the table appeared three plates of cabbage soup with pork, salmon, and three glasses of stewed fruit.

"Well, traveller, shift yourself over to us."

The lad smiled, eagerly grabbed his onion and the bread with mustard, and sat down at the table.

"That's yours. Devour it."

"Oh, well!"

"Dig in. You earned nothing today?"

"My pocket was picked."

"Really. Much?"

"Fifteen hundred."

"Gee! And where is your shirt?"

"I dress specially like this."

"What's that?"

The lad leaned toward us and whispered, making a frightful face:

"I'm working. You see I work for the agencies, in criminal investigation.

45

A disguise, you see? I have a mission, brother . . . hm-m." He ate at the same time, choking, burning his mouth, spilling cabbage soup on the table. "Found one gang; the chief of the criminal investigation department said: expose them-10,000 on the nail for you! I'm watching . . . hm-m . . . But they caught me and put me in the cooler . . ."

"Who? The gang?"

"No! The police! There are blockheads here in Irkutsk. I travelled in a freight car for forty-eight hours. And they say: from which children's home have you run away? I mustn't lose the trail . . . I banged my fist on the table."

"Don't rush, don't hurry, give way."

"I'll call up the chief, I'll tell him and the dust will fly. He'll give it to them. I phoned in the morning, he wasn't in, had left on a mission. Have you some small business here at the construction site? Well, I have now arrived. Only psst! We'll catch them, don't worry."

"Hm-m," said Leonid, scratching the back of his head. His eyes looked pensive, serious. "My word, those monsters, again salmon without a smell. Oh, those . . . !"

I tasted it. It was ordinary fresh fish.

"I so much wanted to show you! When it smells a bit—ah, that's a dish!"

"Never mind, the pork is a bit tainted," I observed.

"Well?" our lad roused himself. "Well? Disgraceful! Stop! We shan't leave the matter here. We'll note it. Waitress! What's the canteen number? The surname of the head cook? Don't want to answer? We'll write that down too . . ."

He pulled out a packet of frayed papers, a yellow pencil, and began to draw up: "Canteen No. 5 . . . dinner . . . disgraceful . . . salmon untainted, tainted pork . . ."

I burst out laughing and nearly swallowed the wrong way. Leonid winked.

"Well, do you have your documents, criminal investigation department man?"

"Everything is here. The duty officer in the department took them

46

away. Well, I don't have them. I have only to phone the chief—they'll return everything, gladly. Oh, they'll be in trouble!"

"And what are those papers you have?"

"Nothing particular . . ."

"House for sale in Kuz'mikha with a cow. Apply to 16 Sadovaia Street." What's that? "Only because departing. Selling six-year old goat with kid, milch, medicinal milk. Telephone . . ." Starting a home of your own, is that it?"

"Oh, no! It's simply, well, it was posted and I thought I would take it down and read it."

"This is stripped off from some poles?"

"Everywhere."

"And this . . . one who is literate is incomprehensible . . . "Who seeks a suckling pig, one and one-half months—two, please come to select." Well, what's this. Have you chosen a suckling pig?"

"I haven't gone yet . . ."

"Listen, and this is sensible, brother! Oh? Understand, Tolia, he goes for such an advertisement, bargains for the goat, house, cow, picks up something while doing so, scrutinizes everyone . . ."

"Oh, yes! All this for the criminal investigation department! Only-shh!"

"Only, brother, you don't look like a buyer or the owner of a suckling pig, The wind whistles under your jacket."

· "I don't do it for myself. My aunt sent me. She's ill, and greedy."

"Ha-ha-ha! Strong chap, bright. Well, O.K., and where will you spend the night?"

"Wherever is suitable . . ."

"The night is cool. It may rain or they may take you for a petty thief again. Take the pencil . . . The yellow one. This when he bought the house, it was attached, yes? Well, write: "Fifth settlement, barracks nine, room five." Ask for me. Leonid. Come for the night, we'll chat, we'll have supper. Perhaps we can fix you up. I tell you this: if you work in my brigade, every day

47

there will be cabbage soup with pork to dig into, and your "criminal investigation department" with it . . . All in all, come for supper!"

"Thank you."

"Simply drop in. What's your name?"

"Sania."

"Drop in, Sania. I'll find a shirt for you too."

"I'll come."

The lad jumped up from the table and, putting his head down, rushed to the door. Leonid pensively struck his spoon on the table:

"The family of some villain and drunkard; the boy cleared out from home and picks pockets. But he's bright . . ."

"Do you think he'll show up?"

"He'll come. I've met so many guys like him. You just pat him, show him some kindness. He hasn't seen it in his life . . ."

A 180-DEGREE TURN

On the crest of the earthen dam we shook the sand out of our boots.

Leonid offered to show me the construction site: "It's all the same to me, I've nothing to do, and it's a long time since I've strolled about"—and the two of us climbed about the hollows and viaducts. We climbed into the ground holes, sat in the units themselves, where soon water will seethe and rotate the blades. We clambered on to the steel reinforcement, slid on the self-propelled excavator, were jolted in the cab of a 25-ton dump truck.

Everyone there knows Len'ka: he is the brigade leader of the carpenters. The drivers stop and offer him a ride, and he agreed to attend a dance with the excavator operators.

Dust, heat, bells, clangs. I wandered, confused and stumbling, behind him, making sense of nothing, not comprehending where the helical chamber is, why they "pour the bosom," but he dragged on and on, shouting:

48

"There it is, the dam! All right! We are on the seabed. Hold it, don't walk, they are blasting there."

Behind the mountains of crushed stone resounded explosions, small rocks flew up: a rock face was being smashed to pieces for the self-propelled excavators. I saw this for the first time, and it seemed to me to be just a movie, or a dream. I felt giddy.

Utterly exhausted, I saw down on a pile of stones. From there everything was visible, as on a map. The construction site sprawled out in a bend of the river. The deepest foundation ditch was dug here—an entire ravine below the riverbed of the Angara—and they enclosed it with dikes.

In the foundation ditch stands the station building—all in scaffolding and iron. Above it, along an overpass, move six gantry cranes. From the building to the Angara the earthen dam on which we were sitting extended for just less than a kilometer. As soon as the building is finished, the dikes will be destroyed—and the water will gush into the foundation ditch-ravine and flood everything. Then they will fill up the dam to the shore, blocking up the Angara—and it will pass through the station, the valley will begin to fill up, and will rise to the crest of the dam at 30 meters. There will be a sea . . .

A sea in the center of Siberia . . .

I, anxious willy-nilly, stood, looked, and for the first time began to grasp the meaning of those astonishing transformations of which I had read and heard more than once—and all the same didn't get especially broken up about. Construction sites, hydroelectric stations, new railways, volunteers travelling to the Virgin Lands and to Siberia . . . A wind of anxiety embracing everyone and everything, a wind continuing an era of great feats and discoveries.

Whoever invented: "Convict Prison Siberia"? A museum term. Thoughtlessness, because of once unsuitable means of conveyance! Now, when Siberia had become close, something had begun that Europe had never seen nor dreamed of even. Old, cramped, habitable, and built up Europe . . . Here, in virgin expanses, they cut again with enormous blows, that's how it is here. A sea in the center of Siberia! . . .

Now it was relatively quiet and deserted at the dam; below sounded

49

noise and bells, the howling of the self-propelled excavators. A long-tailed, grey bird descended, sat on a little rock, and scrutinized us, cocking its head.

"Birdie," said Len'ka affectionately. He was so funny, with a boxer's physiognomy and a soft voice. "Birdie . . . Ah, you, my foolish one! You're interested, are you? Well, what are you looking at? . . . They often fly here. All the wild life and birds have left, but these birdies not. They flutter down to you on the steel reinforcement, sit down, and watch; What are these people doing? A good little bird . . . But all in all, Tolia, you should join my brigade."

"What?"

"How about it? Don't you like it with us? You're bright! What are you going to do at Bratsk? Everyone jumps this way and that, in private they sit about. We'll manage there too! Here something is happening! Soon we'll clam the Angara. It's fast and strong—look what will be! Stay; true you're naive. We'll dam it and go together to Bratsk. There's nothing there yet, they're cutting the forest, but here is what's most important. Let's go! Come join my brigade. We'll live together!"

"Listen, I don't even know how to hold an axe in my hands . . ."

"I'll teach you! Scarecrow, let's go! Over there's our block, look, they're hammering over there. I'm going to hammer there at night: tap-tap, tap-tap . . ."

"You, Len'ka, are actually in love with the construction site, as with a girl."

"Even more. You don't understand anything . . . Over there, look, are the houses which I have built. I've been here since the first day. A barn stood there, understand? . . . All the timber, all the sheathing went through these hands . . . Oh! Are you coming to join the brigade or not? And now let's fly headlong below to my place."

Pushed by him, I actually flew; again our boots were completely full of sand, but we didn't shake them out. Len'ka literally carried me to the administration house of the Hydroelectric Power Station.

"Hey, wait a minute. Not right away! . . . How could I . . ."

"Shut up! . . ."

He applied directly to the chief engineer, began to describe how the brigade needed people, and I was from Moscow, with a secondary education, was eager to work, had just arrived, and on and on . . .

The chief, very busy, smiled and glanced at me:

"Now, Lenia, the urgent need is not for carpenters, but concrete workers. Fourth sector, Moskalenko's brigade of concrete workers. If you agree, dash off an application."

As if in a trance, I wrote at Leonid's dictation: "I request to formalize me . . ." The chief scribbled on the corner: "No objections"—and we rushed out. We filled in something more in the personnel section—without red tape, without waiting, quick as lightning.

"There, a paper to get accommodation; start work on Monday, second shift. You'll receive work clothes."

We left the office, and only now I dared to open my mouth. What? Already I had a job? . . . And the Bratsk Hydroelectric Power Station?

"I tell you, we'll still get there!" Len'ka yelled happily in my ear. "Dance, naive lad, fools have the luck: do you know what the Moskalenko Brigade means? It's the most outstanding brigade. They've had the banner for six months and cede it to no one!"

"Len'ka! But I have no idea whatever as to what concrete is!"

"You'll learn, you worrier. You won't get rich baking pots. They took you at once without any fuss—which means they are in urgent need. You'll learn in two minutes. You have a secondary education, Muscovite! You see! And were it not the Moskalenko Brigade, I wouldn't let you go to another! Look how the engineer grasped it: at once to the best brigade. I worked you round for your best interest . . . O.K., it's all the same to me, you are my godchild, the twelfth already!"

"Oh, you . . . devil!"

"And what have you been thinking? There's nothing for me to do, I'll hang about you as a favor at the construction site? We won you over from Bratsk, won you over! Hurrah!"

SISKIN, WHERE WERE YOU?

Only now did I begin to comprehend what had happened. I pondered it on the double because with the precious paper: "We request you to accommodate concrete worker of the fourth sector . . ."—Gosh!—with Len'ka I went cross-country through broken terrain to the house administration.

We took a short-cut along a dike, slipped by across the face of a self-propelled excavator while that cumbersome machine was awkwardly turning to the other side, jumped every other step up the wooden stairs coming out of the foundation ditch . . . Then the city and behind it a marsh with a herd of goats. Across the marsh a footbridge had been laid on piles, and the planks squeak gaily and bend underfoot. Farther on, up a hill, is the fifth settlement—rows of identical barracks, gay to look at, but as similar to one another as toy soldiers.

The house administration was in a little temporary hut. On the outside an ordinary izba, but within there were inkspotted tables, abacuses, telephones, the smell of blotting paper and registers; busy employees buried their noses in ruled books. There was a long queue at the door with the sign "House Administration."

"We . . . ah . . . we want to see the superintendent."

"She's not here, she went to get the linen. Wait."

"Will it be for long?"

"No."

After our run we couldn't catch our breath. We sat down on stools. Well, what the hell, we'll wait. It's so hot . . .

"Listen, this is disgraceful. I have a family of six, and you are keeping us in a hostel."

"Wait, they'll give you house 18 and move you to the first settlement."

"You promised me house 6, house 12, and house 13. I'll go to the head of the construction site. How long will this farce drag on? I've just come in from the night shift and instead of resting I'm obliged to leave no stone un-turned from the very morning."

"I told you: they'll give you house 18 . . ."

"To hell with 18, move us into 13!"

"13 is full up."

"And why have you moved the mechanic there? He arrived after me and already lives there. His sister is a superintendent, right? And I have a family . . ."

"You're not the only one. Everybody has a family."

"Where's the house-manager?"

"The house-manager is at the housing committee planning meeting. You can wait and tell him your claims, but I'm the bookkeeper, don't interrupt my work."

"Who's next to see the house manager?"

"There's one old woman, she ran to the housing committee to smash the chief's windows."

"We've been moved into a kitchen," smiles a good-natured stout chap. "Three families, all recently married. They've hung curtains. Night comes—they all wait to see who will fall asleep first. Oh, you've paused! Labor produc-tivity is falling because of this!"

Everyone is guffawing.

"How quick they are to tax bachelors, but an apartment for newly-weds—not on your life!"

"Where is the house manager?"

"I answered you in the Russian language: at a planning session of the housing committee. Wait."

The queue lengthens, drones, and Len'ka and I were glad we only wanted to see the superintendent.

We sit for a long time, entered into the family affairs of half the settle-ment, and felt sorry for the martyr-bookkeeper who in the house manager's absence was obliged to listen to all the housing misfortunes and needs.

About two hours later a young, attractive woman, quiet and unhurried, showed up.

"Oh, Vera, they've brought staple linen into the manufactured goods shop! . . . Looking for me, boys? Give me the paper. Just one of you?"

"One. We want him in our house!"

She scribbled something:

"That's all. Now you need a visa: "Move in". Go to the house manager, and then I'll issue linen to you."

"To the house manager? Oh . . . couldn't we first have the linen and then see him?"

"No, it's not allowed, that's the procedure. Without a visa I can do nothing. No. no, boys."

"Oh, darn it! . . . We went to the tail of the queue. For two hours we sat, and we could have joined the queue as the first. Now there was no pity in our hearts for the bookkeeper."

"Where's the house manager? When's he coming?"

"I told you in the Russian language . . ."

"You tell me in Turkish!"

"Don't be rude!"

"But we need to see the house manager!"

So we listen for another hour. Len'ka suggested that at the planning session of the housing committee they are deciding a four-kilometer long question and had only reached the two-kilometer mark, so one must do something about it. God bless Len'ka, without him I would have been lost.

"Comrade bookkeeper, what is the house manager's surname?"

"Siskin."

We went to the housing committee.

For a long time we strayed among the barracks. Finally we found it. A little izba, abacuses, telephones, bookkeeper, a queue at the door with the sign "Head of the Housing Committee." The window-glass was intact.

"What planning session?" sincerely asked the local bookkeeper. "There is no planning session today."

54

"But perhaps Siskin is in the head's office?"

"The head himself isn't here, he's at a conference in the administrative-economic section. I believe Siskin was just here but went back to his house administration."

What a pity! While we ran, Siskin it turns out already was there. Quickly to the house administration! We arrived on the run, out of breath.

"Has he come?"

"No."

"You know he is probably in the store," said the bookkeeper, pitying us.

It was unbearable. Heat. Stuffy, quarrels in the queue . . . We ran to the store. Closed for lunch. In the other one—not a soul.

Damning Siskin, frothing, we returned to the izba.

"Oh! Probably he's in the club at the fifth settlement: they are repairing it," guessed the bookkeeper.

Well, all right! We aren't going to give up until we find Siskin. In the club truly everything was upside down: the painters were painting the walls. They hadn't seen Siskin. We were exhausted. Dust, heat; lazy dogs sprawl on the grass; goats lie in the road and chew, chew; the kids had wooden bars on their necks to prevent them from sucking milk. Someone's young wife launders a child's loose jacket in the shade of a barrack and hangs it on the clothes line.

Then Len'ka spat, swore, and said that he had one idea left. We once again went to the house administration and found out Siskin's home address from the bookkeeper. He lived on a street with a poetic name: Composer Street, 50, a detached house.

Thirty persons remained in the queue to await our return. If we brought in Siskin dead or alive, they will allow us to be first. Only one visa was needed: "Move in," two words, a few flourishes. There were places in the hostels, there was linen, there was a superintendent, but she will leave to look at staple linen . . . Siskin is utterly indifferent as to who I am: he won't ask for my biography, he merely dips his pen and puts down: "Mo-ve-in."—as he has done

100, 200, thousands of times. But for this his hand is required. Only his most august hand. That's the procedure. Dead or alive!

And we found him.

One couldn't say he was completely alive, but in any event he was mobile. The legendary Siskin, drunk as a lord, stood knee-deep in mud behind the fence of his detached house on Composer Street No. 50—and watered his individual vegetable garden from a hose.

Well, tell me, what kind of idiot waters a vegetable garden in such heat? You know all the cabbage is burning up!

WHERE IS THIS STREET, WHERE IS THIS HOUSE?

Dances were held in the moonlight, right in the middle of Mukhina Street, on the pavement. All the girls seemed to be unusually pretty. There was the aroma of perfume, hay, and fresh milk: the women at this hour were milking their cows.

I danced with a girl called Tonia. She is slender, strong, and well-proportioned. Her face is narrow, with a sharp nose. Large eyes, wide-set; her braids are around her head in a wreath, and very lovely eyebrows—thin, dense, as if drawn with charcoal. I silently called her: "Tonia with the falcon brows."

Perhaps I had fallen in love a bit, because I forgot about Len'ka and that tomorrow I would receive work clothes and undergo a training course—I escorted Tonia home to her hostel on Maritime Province Street, and then went on alone, breathed, waved my arms, and sang. How wonderful it was!

At night the settlements are empty and silent. The dogs bark; heels sound resonantly on the footbridges across the marsh; a solitary lamp weakly illuminates the rusty water and hummocks, rows of windows are lit up in our barracks.

Suddenly I stopped, perplexed. All this was fine, but . . . which barrack was mine? I know it's not the first one, but which: the second, third? And in which row? An unpleasant chill sobered me up; I had forgotten the number.

There was no one in the house administration now from whom I could find out. Should I knock on someone's door and ask? Ask what? "Tell me, please, where is the house in which I live?"

I began to walk crossways about the settlement, trying to recall some sign. But all the barracks were twins: with identical little porches, identical doors, even the little roadways leading to them were identical.

This was some kind of nightmare. I rushed endlessly to doors, was frightened by doubts, and scurried back. Aha, I remembered! If one enters my house, immediately in front of the entrance is a door with the inscription "Drying Room."

In the first house I decided to enter my eyes saw at once the sign "Drying Room." I walked along the corridor counting the doors—luckily I remembered my door was the third on the left. Here it is! I opened it wide and . . . suddenly drew back. In the room, full of steam, a fat auntie clad only in a shirt was bathing some kids. No, obviously this wasn't it.

Lingering between houses, I sat down on the grass and readied myself for the worst. I faced spending the night out in the open.

I, a concrete worker of the fourth sector of the Irkutsk Hydroelectric Power Station, who has his own bed, two sheets, a pillow, and a warm blanket!

On this incredible day I had run around so much, was so tired and could visualize a pillow so clearly, that I leapt up and decided not to cease searching even if it lasted until morning.

A system was needed. The houses on the edge were of no interest to me—and this meant already some had been eliminated. The one in which the auntie is bathing the children also was out . . . However, which one was it? I had forgotten!

Cursing myself for inattention, I began to look for the house. Once more I called on the auntie: she already had dressed the children. Having caught sight of me, she cheerfully cried out, grabbed some finery, and ran on my heels to the porch itself. In another house I intruded into a celebration: music, songs, the clatter of dishes. A joyous drunken company of people celebrated my arrival as though they had been waiting the entire evening just for me. They grabbed my arms, sat me down at a table, and to this day I feel ill at ease for having refused.

In the next house the third door on the left was opened by a sleepy unshaven man who said that he knew me and if I ever again called on his wife, he would break my ribs.

My house I found long after midnight in the next row. This morning I went to the store, but remembered last evening's nightmare, came back, and with a lump of plaster drew an X on the door.

OUR GLORIOUS COMMUNE

In the fifth grade I had imagined that the workers, those who build large electrical power stations, were giants wearing electro-welders' masks, completely occupied in socialist competitions and the fulfillment of their percentage of the norms.

But they are people, simply people, the same as I am: they are Len'ka the Siberian, Tonia with the falcon brows, Dima Strepetov on the train, my neighbors in the hostel. Here I was simply accepted, almost indifferently: a new inhabitant, well, O.K., they asked from what sector I came and invited me for soup. Here are those with whom I will live.

PET'KA. He is an electrician from our fourth sector. Stocky, solidly built, strong as a wrestler, with long arms. In his pockets he has short wires, insulation, safety fuses, and pliers, and on the first day I found him at his favorite occupation: he was sewing on a button with the aid of pincers and copper wire. Pet'ka explained that it would be stronger and anyway there was no thread in the house.

Yesterday Pet'ka mobilized our blankets, hung them tightly over the window, and offered a choice: either sit in total darkness or clear-off.

The fact is that he was an amateur photographer. And I understood that this good life awaits us now and forever more . . .

Pet'ka belongs to that category of especially avid amateur photographers which does everything by themselves. Only his "Smena" camera is factory-made, but everything else—enlarger, lamp, bath, little tanks, developers, fixing agents—he does with his own hands. To get a drink of water one first must wash the cup with hot water. Chemicals everywhere: on the table, in the cupboard, under the bed. The snapshots have to dry, and Pet'ka spreads them out on our beds and pillows. They must be glossy, and he fastens them on our window panes. Then the snaps don't come unstuck, so two panes are broken and covered with our own towels (Pet'ka needs his own to wipe his hands).

We have two plates for food, the rest being used for photography. In the morning I accidentally salted the *kasha** with hydrosulphate and couldn't understand for a long time why there was such a strange taste. Pet'ka removed the *kasha*, threw it in the rubbish, and calmed me down by saying that hydrosulphate is not very poisonous and promised to do some marvelous photos for me. He promises everyone.

KUBYSHKIN. He is called Sergei, but the name doesn't suit him. He is just Kubyshkin, and everyone calls him by his surname. Quiet, independent, a passionate rummager: he is constantly rummaging for something and rummages in his belongings, books, dishes. Even when he sits motionless on his bed it seems he is rummaging around and grumbling.

Kubyshkin, firstly, is a fitter; secondly, a great idler. He comes home only to rummage about and have a snack. Sometimes, in Pet'ka's words, he doesn't even stay the night.

The subtlety is that Kubyshkin is now engaged in a delicate matter: he is going to get married. Pet'ka advised me at once that Kubyshkin is a great chap, but a fool: he is as poor as a churchmouse and has fallen in love with the same kind of girl from the hostel. If Pet'ka were to marry, he would take a

* (Dish of cooked grain or grouts—transl.)

bride from among the Irkutsk kulaks, with an Izba and cows, equip himself with a first-class photo laboratory, drink tea with cream in the mornings, and eat an egg with sausage.

The marriage evidently is moving ahead because Kubyshkin, on every occasion, says: "Galia and I." In the evening this Galia came home with him for the first time, and we inspected her mercilessly.

She turned out to be small, frail, and shy. Her face was completely unattractive, colorless, grey. She didn't know what to do with her hands, and they were clumsy and red. She is an unskilled laborer, and has only a fifth-grade education.

When the door opened, Kubyshkin entered first—proud, independent, offhand, and immediately behind him, behind his back, came quiet frightened Galia. We sat her down on a stool. Kubyshkin rummaged about independently, and conversed loudly with us:

"Tomorrow we'll deliver a large pulley-block. Pet'ka, where's the mirror? Have you a razor blade? Stepan has gone on leave, have you heard?"

And he sat on the edge of the stool, round-shouldered, and silent, as if she weren't present. So very quiet, modest, defenseless, and all the time tried to hide her feet in worn out twisted shoes of prewar style.

Kubyshkin and Pet'ka had a long talk about everything, looked at recent photographs and negatives, and then Kubyshkin glanced at the wall and said:

"Galia, let's go."

She roused herself, whispered "Good-bye," and left behind him, devoted and obedient.

ZAKHAR ZAKHARYCH. The third inhabitant of our room is unusual. He is sixty years old. Imagine a tall, smart-looking elderly man of military bearing. Add to it a completely snow-white head. But the grey hair isn't in keeping with him—it is flaxen hair which one would like to braid. No. Zakhar Zakharych can't be called old: he always is clean-shaven, his facial features are strong and energetic: a fleshy nose. Our Zakhar Zakharych is the driver of a seven-ton dump truck, a MAZ-205, a man with forty years' experience as a driver.

I still hadn't come to know him because the greater part of his day he spent at the garage, and he even worked on Sunday. Pet'ka recounted that he was an old communist, that about 1918-19 he drove a tank in the revolution and was a volunteer in the war on the Leningrad front. His entire large family had perished in Leningrad during the siege and since then he has been alone.

The garage was some distance away, and Zakhar Zakharych leaves the house at 6:00 a.m.: we leave the radio loud speaker switched on for him at night. He is very disciplined, his bed perfectly made; he speaks in a thick pleasant bass with confident rumbling notes. But he became completely helpless when he undertook to heat up soup.

We all must prepare soup. We are a commune. We all pool together and buy groceries, and we prepare it in turn. Actually, as Pet'ka explained, taking turns is not always adhered to: he who first arrives and is hungry does the cooking. *Kasha* with hydrosulphate was my first achievement in this field.

But Zakhar Zakharych doesn't know how to cook, and Pet'ka mocks him:

"Not that way, not that way. Now chop the onion. Where's the knife? Gracious, where's the knife? Lord, you are muddle-headed!"

"Petro, look, is that enough groats?"

"You are out of your mind! That's for a full platoon! Where did you pour it from, put it back! Quickly!"

"Never mind, Petro, it will become thicker . . ."

"How thicker, it won't cook. Get a spoon before they're soaked. Where's the spoon? Get a move on, there's the onion, chop it more quickly, the fat's burning!"

Dinner is cooked with a scandal, but later the contents of the saucepan are poured into a deep bowl, from half-soup, half-kasha comes an appetizing steam, and we sit around in a circle with clean spoons and begin to "dish it up." The soup-*kasha* is greasy, thick, and substantial. I give up first, then Kubyshkin, but Pet'ka and Zakharych sit to the end, lovingly scraping with their spoons and once in a while uttering phrases:

"Suppose one should add some bayleaf?"

"It's fine . . . Leave it as it is."

"All right! . . . But the potatoes are overcooked."

After this follows tea, which we drink from half-litre glass jars because the cups are filled with chemicals. It's brick-tea, thick, turbid, somehow substantial, after which it's almost impossible to breathe, and we loll about—each on his own bed.

"Well, it seems we've eaten a bit too much," says Zakhar Zakharych, opening his belt.

"Gosh," asks Pet'ka, "have you driven "Fords"?"

"I've driven them. I even drove the old ones, those jalopies, perhaps you've seen them in pictures?"

"Aha. And Studebakers?"

"Along Lake Ladoga. I changed three of them."

"And Willys?"

"I've driven them. That was in Germany. I drove a general."

"Why don't you marry again? Look, Kubyshkin is going to be married."

"No, Petro, that's not for me. Anyhow I've lived my life . . ."

BAPTISM

In new black overalls and new rubber boots I appeared at the works superintendent of the fourth sector. They were sitting on logs and rocks, or lay about, devouring sunflower seeds in the same overalls, and several men were smoking and laughing. I shyly approached and asked one of them whether this was the Anna Moskalenko Brigade. He was a red-head, like the sun, and moreover he stammered.

"I'm going to work with you."

"W-well, O-O.K." said Red indifferently and turned away, rolling a small cigar.

I offered a "Belomor" cigarette. This puzzled him somewhat, and he hesitated an instant whether to take it or not.

"Slip a "Belomor" to everyone, you'll lose your trousers," he growled discontentedly and took it. "But my wife d-doesn't allow me to have cigarettes, she hisses, the bitch."

After that he finally and irrevocably turned his back on me.

To tell the truth, I had expected anything but such a reception.

The four o'clock whistle blew. The workers began to assemble in small groups and left for home. But we all sat, no one thought of moving, they scratched themselves and giggled. I thought: "This is a job! And they call this the best brigade? How strange."

Finally, the brigade leader appeared—a small, dark-complexioned, snub-nosed woman. She was so puny and tiny that I wanted to rub my eyes: could this be the brigade leader of the concrete workers at such a construction site? She was lost among all the others, climbed up on a rock so she could be seen, and finishing an argument with a foreman ("Your carpenters aren't my concern. Disperse them!), began to divide us up:

"Today, everyone in the same places as yesterday. Mashka to the big pulley-block, Dashka—to the floodgate . . ."

"O-oh, a-gain the floodgate. A plague on your floodgate!"

"Get up, Dashka! Enough of your lying about . . . cow!"

They rose unwillingly, took their shovels, and wandered off in various directions. And I suddenly felt so bored, so depressed!

"I'm new here," I said, no longer able to stand it and thinking they hadn't noticed me.

"I see. Dashka! Tell Efremovich that he . . ."

How indifferent they all are, how rude! They virtually ignore the brigade leader; they wave their hand as if to indicate O.K.! And Moskalenko takes no offense, as if this were expected. She dispersed them irritably, swearing, and climbed down from the rock.

"Your name is Anatolii? Nikolai! Take him to the first crane, to the receiving area."

"Let's go," muttered Nikolai, without glancing at me.

He wandered lazily along the squared beams, over stones, completely un-

63

interested whether I was following him or not. We crossed over a knee-deep puddle, climbed a stairway. Higher, higher. Grey walls flashed by, interlaced steel girders, platforms; we stooped, slipped, climbed and climbed . . . I tried not to look at the ground: it had remained far below, and we became entangled among the interlacing of steel and timber, and there was no return. And suddenly . . . the sky appeared!

Oh, what a height it was! We had climbed out of a hole, it turned out, at the very top of a viaduct, wide like a bridge. Directly before us stood the most immense gantry crane, and its arm, it seemed, clung to the clouds, and at the very tip fluttered a red flag.

The viaduct was empty, only a tub for concrete lay there—an enormous steel box on slide rails affixed to the hook of the crane.

"You see the t-tub?" Nikolai said.

"Yes."

"As the vehicle pours into the tub, you clean the baskets with a shovel and yell to the crane operator "lift." Understood?"

"That's clear."

"That's all. Write down the vehicle numbers and who did how many turns, and report it to the brigade leader. There's the shovel, and I'll leave—he concluded his training instruction.

He disappeared into the same hole from which we had emerged, and I looked about in puzzlement holding the shovel, approached the tub, and touched it. Oh hell! Wasn't that a dream? They stick it at me: I clean it and yell "lift" . . . The awesome crane stood before me like a dinosaur, and I in comparison was an ant. And if suddenly I did something wrong? Did I know how to do it? I became frightened. Some beams are lying there, crooked, why these beams? Aha, so the vehicle wheels travel on them . . . That damned redhead didn't tell me. Why did he dislike me?

Where does the crane carry the tub? Aha, there are our girls in the midst of boards and steel, as in a cage, busy with the block, they pull the cables . . . My heart stopped. Tonia! Tonia with the falcon brows. My God, it's her! Is

64

she in our brigade? She is, and red-headed Nikolai is crawling down there, he waves his hands . . . From above everything is quite visible.

Red–headed Nikolai had given me a heavy cement-encrusted shovel with a gnarled handle. How fortunate that I in my time had learned to work with this instrument of production! Every autumn our entire school planted garden trees. Vic always did a bunk, was "sick", but I liked to dig holes, to dig until the sweat poured down my back. Oh, did I think that I would rake in concrete with a shovel at the Irkutsk Hydroelectric Power Station? And now it comes in handy . . .

Sounding like a pigeon, the first vehicle with concrete raced toward me along the viaduct to the bridge. Well, hold on Tol'ka!

CAN I ENDURE IT OR NOT?

Work had begun! I had started to sweat in the very first minutes. Everything turned out to be simple and incredibly difficult. The vehicle flew along, spilling the grey dirty mortar, travelling backwards on a beam, emptied the baskets, and I threw myself into the dirt itself, into the baskets, scraped out the concrete stuck in the corners with the shovel, heavy, sticky, like a clay mixture, I rolled around together with it in the tub, floundered there, drowning in concrete, jumped out, carrying pounds of it in my boots, and yelled:

"Lift! Go on!"

The crane clanged, tugged, the tub stood on end, and flew into the sky. Out of it rained down stones and mortar: I ran back to the barrier itself, and there somewhere below red-headed Nikolai directed the tub, opened it, but I didn't look—I feverishly recorded the vehicle number, made a cross, dragged away the beams so they didn't become fixed in the concrete, and there it comes already, empty. It banged with all its might and dragged along the viaduct. I throw myself toward it, holding against it with all my strength, and lead it to the place. "Toot, toot, toot-toot!"—signals the crane operator. Farther, farther! Away! I jump aside, and the tub drops heavily on to the slide rails.

"Let's go!"

The vehicle rushes up, I drag the beams.

"Backwards. Drop it!"

I got blisters on my hands in the very first minutes. Hurt by the gnarled shovel handle, my hands were bleeding. I sweated in the heat, wanted to drink something, began to choke. And the vehicles came, came . . . I jumped aside, cried "lift", pulled . . .

No, what's heavier than concrete! A sticky grey mass mixed with stones. A full shovel is almost impossible to lift. If only there were a minute's rest! Never: a row, a line of vehicles.

. . . Already I was unable to lift the shovel and thought with terror: "what if I can't endure until the end of the shift? Suppose I fall under the tub?" My heart chilled. I must endure, must cope! The drivers were various: some happy, reckless—they opened the buckets while in motion so that the concrete almost flew out; others slowly joined up with it, their concrete rather oozed out, and half of it stayed in the bucket. I waved and waved, almost twisting my arms. Oh! What a job!

I must endure, I must hang on. Endure!

The blood from my hands I wiped on my trousers, felt no pain, salty perspiration poured into my eyes and caused them to smart painfully, and there was nothing with which to wipe them: everything was soggy from the mortar and sweat. My hair was entangled and fell into my eyes. Endure, endure!

An hour passed, then a second and a third . . . I was creeping under the tub, forgetting about the danger. The crane operator signalled with displeasure and stopped. When does the break come? When will the number of vehicles coming be reduced even slightly? But they came and came . . .

Could I last?

66

DOWNPOUR

Just then a thunderstorm crashed out. Low, ashy, threatening clouds flashed by; they took over the entire sky. The sun twinkled and dimmed, red, and was wholly extinguished, and night came. Lightning flashed above the very arms of the cranes, the cloudburst lashed down, drummed on the head, penetrated with cold throughout. Here, on the viaduct under the heavens, I was as if on an open stage. I looked about: everything was obscured by a bluish-grey sheet of rain, thousands of raindrops pour down and splash along the viaduct, the lightning flashes, and it seems to smell of sulphur. The vehicle headlights were switched on. It rains and rains.

Soaked to the skin, stupefied, the water streams and goes into my eyes! The rain refreshed me, and suddenly I understood that I would endure. I would last!

The drivers it seemed also had become excited. I glanced upwards—the crane operator in the cabin grinned and nodded approvingly: let's go, let's go!

So that's it, this colossus of a crane, which up to now I had seen only in pictures, and I don't even believe this is it—and me! It obeys a wave of my hand, lifts the tub like a feather when I cry out "lift," and carefully puts it down with light jerks when I order it "down." The machine listens to me! I'm not afraid of it!

I recalled how one runs a long-distance on the race track and how you feel after half the distance: everything, and then you collapse. And if you take control of yourself, a second wind comes. The rain brought me a second wind!

Strength, strength! For the first time in my life I understood, I felt, what real work is, in the breeze, with salty sweat in one's eyes. The drivers were gaily shouting something—above the noise of the rain I didn't hear it. Below Nikolai, pressing his hands into one fist, raised them above his head, doubtless saying: fine, your work is all right. Here before my eyes the concrete is being transformed into bridge piers—I also had seen them only in pictures. All the concrete passes through my hands. The work of the entire brigade depends on me, and on the brigade, the Irkutsk Hydroelectric Power Station. Well! . . .

Downpour. Night, lights. Spotlights shine and penetrate the rainy haze. Thunder. Excited people, off-color jokes. Oh, give us mountains, we cut through mountains!

The people work, they do everything necessary. I am stupefied and drunk, as from wine. But they simply work, as if everything were as it should be—rain, wind. Red-headed Nikolai potters about below, pulls the tub by the rope; in the glare of the spotlights the girls bend down and up: no matter how much concrete I give them, they put it in; it goes into a bottomless pit. And it seemed to me in these moments that they, these people—drivers, cranemen, our concrete workers—are somehow transformed, beautiful, not petty and indifferent, as I had seen them up to now . . .

The work proceeded well, I was ready to sing and regretted the rain was stopping. All the same, being soaked to the skin, why not go on bathing? How much time had passed in this thunderstorm? An hour, two, a hundred, eternity?

At this instant the flow of vehicles ceased. I was even frightened. It became quiet all of a sudden, and one could hear how the few last raindrops splashed on the platform. I glanced upward—and the crane operator had vanished from the booth; the control levels protruded, but no one was there. What had happened?

Anna Moskalenko appeared on the viaduct. She was soaked as I; her skirt slapped against her thin legs.

"That's all, Anatolii," she said businesslike. "Give me the list of how many trips there have been?"

We counted the crossmarks. There were ninety-eight.

"Oh, almost a hundred," Moskalenko said regretfully "And on that crane, sixty. Well, go on and turn in the shovel."

Suddenly she turned around quickly, frowned, and intently, almost irately, looked me in the eye:

68

"Was it hard?"

"Oh, no . . . at first it was hard, and then things got going," I muttered. "I could even do another shift now! I even wondered why there were no vehicles?"

"H-mm. Well, all right. You'll get used to it," she said, for some reason a little sadly. "Go, rest."

She ran nimbly down the stairs, and I took a step . . . and suddenly reeled: my legs were trembling.

THE WOODEN STAIRS

Now I don't remember very well how I descended from the viaduct, how I turned in the shovel, and why the mittens turned out to be under my belt. They were bloody.

People hurried along the roads out of the foundation ditch. Our brigade dispersed and disappeared like invisible beings. New unfamiliar people walked about and carried boards. Doubtless both red–headed Nikolai and Tonia with the falcon brows had left. I wandered alone through the squared timbers on the bottom of the foundation ditch toward the canteen. I didn't feel like eating but understood that I had to eat something.

Dump trucks passed by, which I dodged, and my eyes were blinded by the headlights and floodlights. There is the ragged index board and behind it a wee shack—the canteen. It is open round the clock.

Were I an artist I would have drawn how the drivers of the 25-ton MAZs arrive for supper. Those enormous machines clustered round the shack like elephants and stood absolutely still, directing their darkened headlights at it. Any of the MAZs could have crushed the tiny canteen with one wheel.

And within, in the shack, the laborers were noisy, banged their cups on the table, peeled sausages, and puffed their cigarettes. I already noticed that the MAZ drivers do not behave like the others: they speak smoothly, with dignity, joke loudly, eat four times as much, and in general feel among other workers as a tankman does among the infantry.

Nonetheless I also was proud of my overalls covered in concrete, my boots, which were bluish grey because of cement stuck to them, and mittens, which I carelessly pulled out of my belt and threw down on the window-sill. I was pleased that in my gait something awkward, broad, workmanlike had emerged . . .

The tables and benches in the canteen had been roughly fastened together from various-sized boards, there were barrels, the floor was littered with butts and paper, the air was blue from tobacco smoke. On the counter side by side lay dust-covered hard chocolate bars and "Vesna" brand candies with popular and necessary articles: open-face sandwiches, breadrolls, milk, herrings, cottage cheese, cutlets. I was dazzled. Beer and wine are not sold in the foundation ditch, but the tap of the kvass* barrel worked constantly, and, poured into cups, it has a color and luxuriant head just like real beer.

I sloshed down some yoghurt with cakes, added a piece of sausage, and drank some kvass. I left with a broad gait and in the darkness collided with a wall that smelt of rubber—I even thought that I had gone out the wrong door. Right against the exit was . . . a wheel my own size. Yet another MAZ had arrived and shoved right against the door itself. I could barely get out. The tiny canteen was completely lost among them, like a child's toy among locomotives.

But I was happy. I wasn't a tourist here. I was a worker. I had become a real worker! My hands dangled like ropes, and they hurt. My boots were unbearably heavy. Oh, why should I relate this? This must be felt by having unloaded 98 vehicles, leaning, staggering from fatigue, from this tiny canteen and running into the wheel of a 25-ton MAZ. I can only say that my whole body was aching and whining, and I surprisingly was tremendously happy.

Stumbling, I crossed the railway track and almost at once was covered

* (beverage made from fermented black bread—transl.)

70

with steam and soot from an express train rumbling through. The dimly-lit windows flashed by, and in a second the red taillights disappeared in the distance. On and on, to Baikal, Chita, Vladivostok . . . But we are building right here!

Who among the workers at the Irkutsk Hydroelectric Power Station doesn't remember the wooden stairs from the foundation ditch to the top of the heap! Here I was dragging myself up it. When hurrying to the house administration Len'ka and I had taken every other step. Now I discerned that the steps were high, and managed to overpower each board by storm. You climb and climb, stop to catch your breath, turn round, and below—the lights . . .

Higher, higher! . . .

Oh, how muddle-headed I am. It's already 2:00 a.m., people are sleeping, and I'm still on my way home from work.

But on the mountain, on the waste land, a crowd moved in a circle like a dark wheel. It sounded as though someone were crying or praying, and then everyone repeated the incomprehensible words, and only a doleful and strange "a-a-a. . ." could be heard. After midnight the Buriat workers assemble for an outdoor party and dance the "iokhar"—a long endless dance, when young men and ladies, arm-in-arm, walk and walk in a circle and sing a monotonous song. Of what they sang I didn't know.

But Len'ka already had talked about the "iokhar," he said that the Buriats gather here three times a week and do the traditional Slavonic round dance until daybreak.

They even come from afar, from the construction site of the aluminium combine, because they dearly love their "iokhar" and it reminds them of their Motherland.

It was so indescribably exciting and melancholy. The light of the foundation ditch, the hum and roar of the vehicles; the anthill among the mounds and swamps is stirring and seething. The wind carries the aroma of cement, of metal, and of the expanses of the river; the far off window-lights in the settlement houses are extinguished. And on the waste land the Buriats dance the "iokhar." I stood aside for a while and listened.

71

Then came a real horror, not finding my mittens under my belt; I had forgotten them in the canteen, on the window!

I returned, then again took the wooden stairway by storm, and went on and on homeward from work. This was one of the most beautiful nights in my life.

End of the Second Notebook

A LETTER FROM VIKTOR RECEIVED
SHORTLY AFTER

"Greetings, old man!

Received your letter, from which I conclude that you're a fool.

It grieves me that you didn't listen to me. Well, work hard. Get on with it!

No, I don't intend to go to Siberia, especially not on the third berth and with ruffians like your three friends. Now I'll explain why.

So then, I went to the Polytechnic to put in an application. I glanced about—my word, a babel! Brother, those crammers sit about, and even those who came from production jobs were shaking. I reckoned it was best to turn back in time. I turned to the Medical. Same thing. To the Financial-Economic. Same thing. To the Peat, etc.—Same thing. Briefly, I went round to a dozen institutions of higher education, but there were no easy areas of study.

A family assembly was enthusiastic about Dad's idea: a trade technical school. Now it turns out that to be admitted there one must pray.

The competitive examination there, Tolia, will probably be O.K. Papa pushed here and there and finally found the way. Ah, what a papa I have! The director of studies there turned out to be an acquaintance—his man, even something of a relative, a distant relative. He threw his money about: an acquaintance is an acquaintance, but money on the barrel. This escapade cost three big ones, but then the appropriate directives were issued.

And you know, Tolia, I have now figured out myself: it's a marvelous Technical School! It graduates workers for the trade network, and in our life this is a treasure. I look at the dacha to the right and am more and more convinced of this . . . It is sad and absurd, when you look at the simpletons, how they cram, preparing for the examinations. Iuna is completely worn out. Yesterday I went with her to the films: I sympathized with her, dragged her into diverting herself a bit. We went to the "Morozhenoe" Cafe, reminisced about you.

She pities you, says that you could work as a loader at her papa's plant. By the way, you should have heard the tone in which that was said! . . .

Well, O.K., write about life there. Have you seen any bears? Have the midges eaten you up?

No, brother Tol'ka!

Stop playing the fool! Enough of pretending that you don't understand the essence of life! I don't know about you, but I'm content. Fine ideas and radiant summits, brother, have been invented specially for naive youths, but the world moves according to other laws, simpler and more specific ones. Of course, fools such as yourself are necessary! Go on, go on, build the hydroelectric station, and by that time others will build themselves a dacha—one near Moscow, another in the Crimea, and yet another at the Riga seaside. These "builders" I understand, but not you.

You'll say I'm wrong? Look about, look about more closely.

74

Where you are, at the construction site, I think all our reality is refracted as in a drop of water. And when you're convinced, well, retreat to hearth and home. For one thing I do praise you: that you travelled without a travel pass. Had you been recruited under a travel pass, you couldn't do a bunk. Good luck! I'm waiting for you.

Destroy this letter. You understand why. It's hard for me, Tol'ka, just as it is for you, but never mind. I'm becoming spiteful. We'll still triumph!

. . . But if you're serious about what you've written to me, then I wash my hands of it. Naive fools like you are supporting the world. Live. Go on, live. Your foolish happiness will pass like a white cloud of smoke. No, why should I? I'll simply laugh at you, I won't take it into my head to convince you. Why do I need to do this?

You, old chap, will be persuaded by life itself."

"P.S. Yes! Mama sends her greetings and asks that when you return to bring a cedar cone (for the mantel, as large as possible)."

THE THIRD NOTEBOOK

THE DEPTHS OF MISFORTUNE?

Oh my hands, my hands!

They ache all day and even more at night. Everything began with the blisters which I inflicted with the shovel handle. Every day I hurt my palms more and more. During the shift while I run along the viaduct, clamber on the machines, gouge the concrete, I somehow forget the pain, don't feel it. But at home I can't stay in one place. This dull, unceasing pain is felt in my forearms and permeates all my muscles. The splits in my palms burn so much that I want to scream. I discovered that cold air soothes. Therefore I walk about the room and wave my hands, and if the pain is too intense, I blow on them. I walk and blow, walk and blow.

Pet'ka looked and ordered me to go to the doctor on sick leave. There was an instant when I started to go. I went down the porch steps, stood for a moment, and returned. How shameful! To work only a few days—and to go on sick leave! No, I'll burst before I'll go to the doctor. I'm a ditherer, a mama's boy. I deserved it! No, we'll see who overcomes whom! my pain me, or I it. I'll not go for anything, I'll blow.

Our young cleaner, quiet and modest Oktiabrina, caught me at this activity. She looked and shook her head:

"Oh, boys, boys. You're going to find out everything. You're going to learn the depths of misfortune in foreign parts."

This offended me. I replied rudely that she had better look for a cap for me in the storeroom since my hair already had turned into concrete from the mortar.

Oktiabrina left silently and brought me her husband's cap—still in good condition and hardly worn. Then I was ashamed, and I promised to bring the cap full of candy for her children.

Every day the same dilatoriness. We come home from work—one must run to the store for food and bread. Then peel the potatoes; take one's turn at the stove; wash shirts and socks. Oktiabrina refuses to launder; she has her own concerns. There are no other women in the house.

The rubber boots and overalls are soaked from the mortar and sweat, are dirty and stinking. They must be placed in the drying room (the stove is heated there, and from the dozens of overalls comes an intolerable stench).

You have no strength to launder the overalls; besides, it is useless. You are content to scrape yourself off in the washroom and hack the concrete out of your ears.

Finally, when you regain a human appearance and your belly is full, you can't do anything more. Pet'ka and Kubyshkin—I'm surprised at them!—put on new suits and quick-marched to an outdoor party until 2:00 a.m. Zakhar Zakharych visits his friend, also an old driver, or invites him himself. There are many places to go: nearby are a club, cinema, library, dances. In the house we even have a Red Corner, and there day and night the lads play billiards. But I lie about the bed and blow on my hands, leap up, and blow.

DAY AND NIGHT

Day and night trains pass by the construction site. Some eastward, ıers, to the west . . . Sometimes their whistles carry to the hostel.

It was evening; the setting sun shone into the window. Zakhar Zakhar-ı had arrived exhausted and fallen into bed. He was breathing regularly and eply on his bed, and I sat at the table, my head in my hands, and thought.

Iuna, Iuna, how far away you are and how alien you have finally be-me!

Once long ago Iuna had fallen ill. We were preparing for the control ams, but she didn't know the rules. Vic, Sasha, and I went to see her. Her ıpa was the director of a large plant, and they lived in a big new house.

We rang for a long time at the enormous oaken door before it opened ıghtly. A woman wearing an apron looked at us suspiciously and in an nfriendly manner. Having examined us from head to toe and blocking the ntrance, she began to interrogate us: who were we, where from, whom did ⁄e wish to see, why, and again, who were we. The door slammed, and we ⁄ere left on the landing, uncomprehending.

Five minutes elapsed. A rustle became audible behind the door. This ime the passage was obstructed by a round, well-dressed woman, Iuna's nother judging by everything. Again an interrogation: who were we, where from, why had we come, what were our surnames. "Wait."

The door banged, and again we stood and waited.

The door opened a third time, and Iuna's mother, her sharp eyes gleaming suspiciously, stepped aside a little:

"Come in. Stand here. Hang your coats here. Put your rubbers there. This way."

Blocking the entrance to the other rooms with her round body and vigi-lantly seeing to it that we—God forbid!—didn't take a superfluous step, she

79

conducted us along the floor-matting to the door of a large room and left it open behind us.

Iuna lay on an ottoman near the wall of this excessively large, empty room, and I thought that to lie ill in such a room was surely uncomfortable and cold. Three chairs already had been placed for us next to the ottoman; we sat on the edge and talked business, only about the control exams. Something was stifling me; I couldn't straighten my shoulders, for some reason couldn't forget that my coat tab was torn off and it might fall down there, in the entrance hall, and listened to the rustles in the corridor.

Iuna said: "Thank you" and asked us to come again, but we didn't know what to talk about; having sat down for five minutes, we hastily said good-bye and left. Only when out on the street did we come to our senses and looked at one another in amazement. Sashka swore, but Vic burst out laughing.

I had another opportunity to visit her again. There was a ski race, and Iuna asked me to come and bring a fastening device. I was no longer perplexed by the admission procedure, but this time I wasn't admitted into the room, but was left to wait in the entrance hall, among the rubbers, at the little round table under the coat rack. Iuna hadn't finished dressing, ran out to see me, asked me to sit down, and again ran away.

Then she brought me a glass of tea and a pile of cakes on a plate. And I, seated beneath the coat-rack, embarrassed because my coat was on, began to drink the tea. I didn't know—perhaps this was necessary, perhaps it was a friendly reception, and I would give offense if I refused . . . The cakes were very tasty, but I noticed this only after having mechanically gulped them down and then was horrified by my bad manners.

No. I'll never forget this. And I'll never forgive myself for not getting up and leaving forever . . .

Why was I in love with her? Those who are in love don't ask this question. She was exceptionally beautiful and intelligent. In school, on the street, in the theatre, at the skating rink—she was transformed. She argued with the boys and got the upper hand; she was always the center of our group and even cut her hair like a boy, and all worshipped her. She didn't like girls, and they in revenge whispered that she dropped atropine in her eyes, which made them so shining and dark. From the seventh grade she dressed according to the latest fashion and conversed about Wilde, Dreiser, and Hemingway. At home they had an enormous library of the most valuable and rare books, but none of us saw the library.

Iuna was a good student, almost straight A's, and she graduated with a silver medal. Every summer her father took her to the Riga seaside and gave her five hundred rubles each month for pocket money.

My mama earned five hundred rubles by laboring all day at a sewing machine in a garment workshop. I begged her for money to go to the movies, but didn't go, saved it, and the next time invited Iuna. It seemed to me that a miracle might happen, that Iuna of the stuffy house with the entrance hall and cakes was unreal. She is intelligent, she is beautiful, she is unpretentious, she is remarkable—I can't stop thinking about her.

But when she went with her medal to the Institute and I saw that her life would be cloudless in the future, then I understood that our paths were very different . . .

I will never see Iuna again. I shan't forget her: that is something one doesn't forget. But now she goes to the movies with Viktor and moreover says that I could have worked at her papa's plant as a loader. And Viktor, too, it seems, has found his path and "treasure" in life . . .

Day and night I hear the train whistles. Some travel eastward; others, to the west. What's going to happen to me. Why have I come here? I can force myself not to whine and not to go on sick leave. But does this make sense?

My path to the world of bright and straight roads, where are you?

THE CONE

Slowly I packed my socks, shirt, and soap in my wornout suitcase, and sat myself down to remember: what was the most important thing I had forgotten? Something very valuable, interesting, and important, and I couldn't recall what. I'll remember later, but it will be too late . . .

Suddenly it seemed to me that Zakhar Zakharych was fixedly and vigilantly watching me. I turned in a flash—he was sleeping as before, the palm of his hand under his cheek; his grey hair seemed dull against the snow-white pillow case.

It was very quiet. I took a breath, looked about the room, looked at my bed. And then I was transfixed: a thought, joyful because finally I had remembered, and repulsive, unpleasant, that I had recalled what I had tried to forget.

The cone! The cedar cone, as large as possible, for the mantel . . .

I sat down on the bed.

And then I saw that Zakhar Zakharych wasn't asleep. He stretched, lowered his bare, sinewy feet to the floor, and yawned sweetly. I slammed the suitcase lid.

"Tidying up?" the old man asked ingenuously. "That's fine . . . Do you remember whether there's any herring left? I want something salty."

Did he see or not? But it's my business, it's all the same to me.

But Zakharych wanted to chat.

"Well, how's the job at the construction site?" he asked, seating himself at the table and starting with the herring. "Are you used to it? Don't miss home?"

"M-m . . ." ("He saw! Else why does he ask!")

"It's always the case. One misses. Believe me, Tolia, when I first came here, I wanted to run away. There was nothing here then, swamp, slush, dirt, fever—oh, blast it! I looked around, scratched the back of my head—and went for the suitcase. Then—no I think, I'll wait a bit, I'll find things out. And to this day I'm finding things out. That's how it was."

"M-m . . ."

"But I . . ." He chose the biggest-bellied fish and skillfully skewered it. "But I look at you: you're having a bad time."

"No, why?" ("No, it seems he didn't see; you can sense by his tone that he hasn't guessed").

"It's hard! But don't worry," he said good-naturedly and tenderly. "Don't worry. Everything will be all right. There . . . hm . . . m . . . see how much caviar the fish has . . . You're doing the right thing, very much so: courageously jumping into life, into the row. Go on being brave! Everyone gets cold feet, but to express fear—that is not worthy for a man. Believe me, I've seen many cowards, and many runaways have visited this very room! It has happened, believe it or not, that one arrives, engages in ruses for a week, gets some blisters—bang! home he goes! You needn't believe me, it's simply amazing! But it's all, I believe, cowardice, it's all fear. The devil only knows what youth are coming to!"

"Zakhar Zakharych, have you been at many construction sites?" I tried to change the subject.

"I have been . . . I've seen it all. What were we talking about? Oh, yes, instability. Insofar as I can tell, the greatest fluctuation of cadres is at the construction sites. This, don't you see, is a touchstone in our life. Construction sites are now the front. Well, at the front there are always deserters and persons with self-inflicted wounds—in other words, no good-for-nothing is going to stay around for long . . . Aren't you ill? Sit yourself down, eat some fish. A glorious dish, democratic, look how good it is! Sit down!"

I felt hot all over. My thoughts sounded an alarm. Did this mean he had seen how I was preparing to leave? Or is this conversation fortuitous? I looked intently into his face, but the old man was quietly cleaning a fish, placed the bones on a newspaper, and began to chat about something else:

"Many bumps occur in life. You'd better be ready. Oh, you'll still get a lot of bumps, until you adjust, be strong—there!—like my fist! But your head will be harder!. . . Why don't you eat something? A bit bored. Best go for a walk rather than rummage about in the suitcase."

"He saw!" I was horrified. "Saw everything. He's toying!"

"I'm going out myself. I slept too much, that's not good."

83

"He didn't see!" I felt a great weight lifted from me. "Otherwise he wouldn't leave me alone."

Zakharych did leave in fact, and I unpacked the socks and soap and put the suitcase under the bed; everything within me was trembling, shaking. I couldn't remain by myself, I couldn't think about anything: it was painful.

I locked the door and knocked on Len'ka's. Fortunately he was at home.

Now and then I visit him. Leonid has a small portable gramophone and a stack of records.

Always he greets me joyfully, ceremoniously seats me on a stool, carefully and solemnly winds the gramophone, checks the needle several times, and only then starts it. He places his hands on the table—large, clumsy, horny hands—inclines his head over them and thoughtfully, sadly listens:

> From the sky fell a star
> on a little wooden shed.
> Give back, sweetheart,
> my ring and handkerchief . . .

This was his favorite pursuit. And I heard for the first time so many Russian songs. In Moscow I had been indifferent toward them. But here, in Siberia, in this men's hostel with its brown rugs and photographs on the walls, with creaking floor and low ceiling, "performed" on this antediluvian hissing gramophone, they touch me and move me to tears by something human, something previously unknown to me, melancholy and enormous. I listened and already it seemed to me: all right, everything will turn out fine. I'll wait, and I'll see what develops . . . I've decided.

I don't know how Len'ka's aesthetic taste was structured, but there side by side with Russian songs peacefully dwell arias from operettas. For example:

> Without women one can't live in this world,
> one can't!

Soon, my angel, you'll be
my little wife.

Len'ka also listens to these sadly, thoughtfully, cheek on his fist, tenderly and carefully cleaning the dust with a special duster and inserting them in their envelopes.

"WITHOUT WOMEN ONE CAN'T LIVE IN THIS WORLD"

Therefore we went to the women's hostel.

Only now did I understand Leonid's cunning tactics: not without reason had he introduced me to Tonia at the dances. Tonia with the falcon brows and Len'ka's love, Tamara, are friends and live in the same room.

We announced ourselves, seated ourselves on the beds, and Leonid at once started to argue with Tamara (this is his manner of courting).

"Oh! The iron has been tied together with thread, blockhead! These women!"

"How it's tied doesn't matter, I did it myself!"

"They'll burn, fool. Should be done with wires, housewife!"

"It's good enough for us, and whoever doesn't like it can ask for a rag for his long nose."

"Ah you, you're a long nose!"

"And you envy me? Well, get lost, why are you sitting about? I'll begin to wield a stick! You came in, so sit and mind your own business."

"Give it here and I'll fix it. Have you any wire in the house?"

"We'll manage without assistants."

Tamara is malicious, energetic, everything is in full swing in her hands; the ancient electric iron is so white-hot that the steam rises in a column from the dresses and only a "zh-rr" is heard when she presses the cloth.

She is the foreman in the third sector; perhaps that's why her tone is so categorical, commanding. She has no braids; pathetic small hairs stick out which are not at all becoming, and all in all she is still a little girl.

"Ton'ka, anything else to iron? All right. Then, scarecrow, take off your trousers."

"You're kidding!"

"Take off your trousers! Who am I talking to? Both of you remove them. When were they last pressed? Seven years ago, after a light rain on a Thursday? Do you think we'll go to the dance with you like this? Remove them, scarecrow, or I'll burn you with the iron!"

"A-a-a!"

Len'ka yelps, Tonia laughs loudly; we submissively remove our pants and, left in our undershorts, are completely disarmed. Steam rises in a column from the pants; sharp creases, like a razor, appear on them. Len'ka bashfully scratches himself, and I look about the room.

How clean it is—almost excessively so! Snow-white little curtains, little napkins, coverlets on the pillows, tiny rugs, paper flowers, pictures on the walls, little mirrors, flasks. In a place of honor a page from a fashion magazine has been pinned up. Also—decorative art! These women!. . .

There are three beds in the room. Tamara lives with her sister. This is a strange, affable, but very shy girl; she has only just finished the tenth grade and is preparing for a correspondence Institute. When I was introduced to her, she timidly withdrew from her corner behind the table, blushed like a red poppy, and whispered without offering her hand:

"Olia . . ."

I extended my hand, she reluctantly offered hers, and while shaking it I felt that her palm was unnaturally narrow and somehow abnormal. I noticed with a casual glance: she had no thumb and index fingers, nearly half her palm was cut off, and there was a gnarled, deformed scar. Somehow all this did not fit with her attractive, tender, light appearance, and I didn't feel so well. Oh, why hadn't Lenka warned me! Olia, biting her lip, shriveled up and darted back behind the table; holding her right hand under the table cloth, with her

86

left she began to thumb through a textbook. She didn't utter a word the entire evening, nor even look at us, as though she weren't present at all.

"You've many books, Tonia. May I look?"

"Look."

"*Scarlet Sails!* Let me read it."

"Oh, no. We only managed to obtain it today . . ."

"Oh, greedy," Len'ka bellowed. "You wouldn't lend us snow in the winter!"

"It's you who are greedy!" Tamara attacked him. "Five years wearing the same trousers. You should be ashamed of yourself. Ugh! Soon there will be holes in them! What sort of worker doesn't earn enough for a suit, drunkard, begger!"

"You're a begger!"

"Who? I? I wish you received as much as we do! Your brigade is worthless! Ton'ka, show them the new dress you bought yesterday . . . There. Like it?"

The dress was darling, with large violet flowers, but obviously very unpretentious, from some inexpensive cloth.

"Ho, ho, ho!" Len'ka rolled with laughter. "It's price—fifty rubles!"

"Fo-ol! This is crepe de fleur. What do you understand? Oh, Ton'ka, I should have taken the silk dress for 500. True, wasn't I a fool not to have taken it?"

Tamarka grabbed a guitar from the bed and, gypsy style, sang in a melodious, ringing, and clear voice:

> Oh-h . . .
> We've got money—the cocks aren't pecking!
> Oh, gypsy girl! Oh, brown girl!. . .

"Life is fine when you are your own master! It is merely considered that if husband and wife, the husband provides for the wife. You're conceited, boors! A woman may earn more than you and live better than you. But later he will reproach you all your life: I provide for you, I make you happy. I shan't marry! I earn for myself—and do what I wish. Tonia and I manage to buy Boston suits and patent-leather pumps! But you'll be in torn trousers. Don't even bother to talk to us then! Oh!. . ."

> At Taganka,
> Where yesterday we met one another . . .

She tossed her pigtails—sun rays sprayed about the little room. She radiated joy, energy, laughter. She winked, stamped her feet, and her thin throat modulated and sang like a nightingale:

> On the little meadow,
> Where only yesterday we parted . . .

In the corner Olia hung her head and closed her ears with her hands. A fat genial face with a devil-may-care forelock dropped in from the hall, raised her eyebrows, grinned, and disappeared. Len'ka, open-mouthed goggled at Tamara with unconcealed admiration, but she danced, sang, twirled in front of us: there, she says, how attractive I am, aren't I?

"OH, YOU NIGHTS, SEAMAN'S NIGHTS"

We walked in the darkness, stumbled, laughed. Tamarka fooled about, resounding throughout the entire settlement—I had never heard such a voice even at concerts:

> Oh you, nights, seaman's nights,
> Only the wind and sea are about . . .

It was completely dark: neither moon nor stars. I held Tonia by the elbow, through her thin violet dress (she wore it to a dance for the first time) I felt the warmth of her live delicate arm; stumbling over potholes, we brushed against one another, laughed, dropped behind.

"Tonia, where are you from?"

"Near Moscow, from Ochakov, along the Kiev railway."

"How did you come to be here?"

"Just like everyone else. Boarded a train and left."

"Did you leave family behind?"

"I did! We have a large family there. Eight daughters, papa, mama."

"Eight daughters?"

"Ah! I'm the eldest, all the others one by one. It was merry! How they began to squeal: Mama, give me! You felt like fleeing from the house!"

"And did you run away?"

"Well, one has to decide something. Now it's easier for them, I send them 400 rubles . . ."

She hesitated as though she had said something wrong and, slightly annoyed, changed the subject:

"I like it here, at the construction site. And you? Have you gotten used to it? Nikolai, the fool, didn't even explain to you what to do. He came and said: he has education, let him use his head. We've already rebuked him . . . You've already coped: we see it's all right, the chap understands.

"You're so unusual . . ."

"How so?"

"Not like yourself. When you're on the pulley, in overalls, you're completely different, a concrete worker! But now—slender, beautiful, elegant."

"Yes?" she sorrowfully, sarcastically asked: "best not to give compliments . . . Let's catch them up? Run!"

On the asphalt at the school the crowd was buzzing as always. It seemed all the youth at the construction site had gathered there. Where did they get their strength? They had worked like devils all day, they should simply stretch out their feet and lie down, but no, they press their clothes, dance until nearly morning, dance until they're dizzy. The accordians scrape, someone merrily

89

"danced a number," some sailors became involved—only where had they come from? We danced round and round in the darkness, virtually by guess-work, and again the aroma of hay and smoke, and hundreds of feet shuffled on the asphalt. Then we went home, again fooled about, prevented people from sleeping. On the wasteland we approached the Buriats. Tamarka audaciously broke into the circle, seized her neighbors by the hand, and danced along with them, immediately in step and rhythm, as if she had been doing the "iokhor" for centuries.

We didn't want to part, it was so nice! We escorted the girls to their hostel. Tamarka shoved Len'ka on to a chalky barrel, and he soiled his hands. We tired of laughing and singing—our chests even began to ache.

Olia opened the door—with blue circles under her eyes, serious, she rubbed her forehead with her left hand; on the table lay ink-spotted textbooks. Tamara went to the kitchen.

"Well, how are we going to make concrete tomorrow?" Tonia said, tiredly throwing her scarf and kerchief on the bed. "We'll want to sle-ep . . . But so what . . . It was fine."

She looked at me with her blue eyes into my very soul. As though we know something the others don't, the idiots. And she quietly asked:

"Right?"

"Right."

"Well, go wash your hands and beat it. March!"

Len'ka and I went into the kitchen. Tamarka was standing at the stove and pouring the rest of the vermicelli from a little bag. She for some reason had grown thin here, wan, wrinkles on her forehead, and only now did I notice with surprise how pallid and thin she is—her bones also were protruding. Wearily she looked at us and said earnestly:

"Well, do you want to be driven out with a broom?"

We said farewell and left. Somehow we were no longer merry. Here, on the staircase landing, at the door with "No. 4", I asked Len'ka:

"What about Olia? What happened to her hand?"

"Well . . . she worked on a rotating device—and it was chopped off. A

90

splendid girl, what a shame! No one looks after her. She decided to retrain herself, stopped working, and as you have seen, is studying. Tamarka supports her, works for the two of them. They are boasting: "We! Crepe de fleur!"— but themselves guzzle vermicelli . . . Let's go home. Thank this house, we'll go to the other."

FRIENDS AND ENEMIES

What should one do when a driver approaches, looks at one with imploring eyes, and says:

"Add on there . . . a few, O.K.?"

In vehicle 00-39 sits a character who reminds one of Uncle Kostia, the train conductor: the same piercing, insolent eyes, only more cunning, more self-assured, and he has gold teeth. Having made ten trips exactly, he paused, opened the door, and inquired:

"Well, how many do I have? Wh-at? According to my count there have already been twelve."

"No, then. Look."

"You count strangely!. . . Put down twelve!"

"I can't, what's come over you?"

He gave me a calculating look, not in a hurry to spit it out.

"M-hm . . . watch out, your pencil will break."

Having quietly closed the door, he suddenly tore away so that the brakes squealed. He was gone for an entire hour, then appeared with concrete and a friendly expansive smile:

"The fifteenth?"

I was enraged. "All the others, you know, already have done twelve and you, eleven!"

He didn't answer nor appear again until the end of the shift. I nicknamed him "the self-seeker with the gold teeth" and am genuinely delighted when I don't see him.

Vehicle 00-77 is driven by a taciturn, middle-aged, hunchbacked man with melancholy eyes. He speaks not a word, dutifully drives the vehicle, painstakingly empties it, and silently drives off. I don't even know what kind of voice he has. For some reason it's difficult for me to see how, so tired and hunched, he manages to sit behind the wheel and see with fixed glance from the cab: what signal I'm going to give. Having made fifteen trips, he got out, silently looked at my pad, sighed, glanced somewhere in the distance, and again resumed hauling. He is very assiduous, but not impertinent and doesn't try to sneak in front of others; although he hauls and hauls without a rest, all the same he somehow receives less than the others. I try to find an error, verify my notations, feel pity for this kind, exhausted man. For some reason I suppose he has a large family and many children. But on my list he is second from the end, after the man with the gold teeth.

Yesterday a newcomer arrived, a Tatar. Obviously he was working his first few days: they had given him the most worthless vehicle, jangling, squeaking, and filthy. Earth had been hauled in it previously, and therefore when the newcomer clumsily raised the dumper, the concrete didn't all come out; it stuck and hung like thick pastry-dough. I gasped. The two of us tried hard for at least a quarter of an hour: we scraped with a shovel, pounded with a sledgehammer. The poor Tatar had exerted more effort than I: he was so conscientious that one wanted to help. In addition, while driving down he had not lowered the dumper. The side had brushed against the edge of a tub—and the hooks of the lower locks were simply ripped off. All of them! That meant repairs.

"Oh, oh, oh!" howled the Tatar, almost crying. "Oh, I made a mistake, oh, I forgot!. . . And I earned nothing today too . . ."

"You made two trips," I said.

"One?"

"Two."

"Thank you . . . ," he bowed, but I turned away.

Genka the gypsy really knows how to work. He's not a gypsy, he's merely tanned, like a Negro, shiny teeth, his forelock blows in the wind, and his vehicle is like a snake. It seems the entire construction site knows him:

"Genka, greetings!"

"Our gypsy with the tassel!"

And he sits behind the wheel like a rider on horseback; he flies—everyone is supposed to give way; girls come along—he brakes and waves with a big smile. He makes thirty trips per shift and still contrives to disappear for an hour or so. And a devil too! He never asks how many trips he's made. He jumps on the beams, dumps the concrete into the tub like a *bliny** from the frying pan, and smiles:

"Properly done?"

"Clean! As though licked by a cow! You grease the dumper, do you?"

"Of course, with "Red Poppy" cream!"

I decided to consult him. What should I do with the others, what should I do with those imploring eyes or their impudent demands? They're besieging me.

Genka listened and smiled crookedly.

"What's it to you—isn't it all the same? It can't be checked, can it? Who the devil can calculate how much I haul in the dumper, a cubic meter or one and a half, a trip is a trip. For us trips count, for you, cubic meters. Your records are based on measures which don't matter to you. It can't work without additions, that's been proved by science. Don't overdo it so that it's too obvious. It would be strange if you didn't make additions. That's all . . . But you needn't add anything for me; listen, I earn enough without your extra marks. O.K.?"

No. Not O.K. I tried to add an extra mark for someone, the others became insolent and demanded even more, two or three each. I was enraged. There was no sense in beginning that! Don't add on—they're venomous, like

* (a kind of pancake—transl.)

93

demons. Add on—they become special friends and beg: just one more, just a little bit!

Today, when the shift changed, I was afraid to look Moskalenko in the eyes. So, how about it? Am I without backbone, or do I have a "kind heart"?

THE SWALLOW'S NEST

The engineer on my crane is a cheerful and good-natured chap, Sasha Gurzii. It was he who smiled at me from the booth on the first day and watched over my every step; in order not to weigh down a muddle-headed, stupefied newcomer, he had given the signals. During the break, he climbed down from his summit, checked the hook, knocked the tub, and smiled good-naturedly:

"How is it? Got used to it? How much longer will I need to worry about you. Why do you take such pains, clean them to the last lump? Observe the rhythm! If you see there is a queue—release them uncleaned, clean them later. Understand? And come along for a cup of tea."

His assistant is a middle-aged, reddish, almost bald Efremovich. This was his patronymic, and everyone calls him that. He's a very pedantic person, fond of reading the newspaper during the break, and talking about politics. While Sasha Gurzii happily handles the levers, Efremovich climbs about the crane, lubricates it, hammers, climbs on to the work bridge, selects a nut and a bit of rope, and brings everything to his booth near the machine—there he has an entire storehouse.

On all cranes there is a shortage of "spiders"—these are special steel loops for the load. A whole bunch of them hang in Efremovich's booth, like harness in the stable of a good boss. It's impossible to steal them because they're directly above the abyss. Only Efremovich himself by some secret means sometimes extracts them and lends them for a jar of grease or bolts in short supply, scolding the supplicant beforehand.

Efremovich is a great philosopher. Once I didn't restrain the swing of the tub and wanted to quiet it more quickly. I leaned over and fell. Efremovich climbed down, took me to one side, and even though vehicles were coming in and the tub was waiting, unhurriedly began:

"What do you regard, my dear lad, as the most important thing in a vehicle?"

"The motor." I was taken aback.

"Fine. Fine. And what else?"

"The steering wheel? The wheels?"

"Oh, you and your "wheels"! Suppose a piglet runs across the road . . ."

"The brakes!" I guessed, impatiently glancing at the tub and understanding nothing.

"Well. Well. Wait, don't hurry. I have a question for you: do the brakes always work without fail or not?"

"N-no . . ."

"So it happens that they do fail?"

"It happens."

"Fine. And do you think our crane has brakes?"

So that was it. That's where he was leading!

"I've understood."

"Not bad! I like clever people. Now mull it over a bit and compare the above with the weight of a tub, three tons, and much will become clear to you. You're welcome again for a cup of tea."

He quietly went off, dragging to the booth a roll of wire which the fitters had dropped. Throughout the entire dialogue Sasha Gurzii patiently sat above and smiled. He certainly had studied Efremovich's character!

I decided to take advantage of the invitation and went, that is, clambered, up the crane during the lunch break. If the viaduct was a dizzy height, then there are no words to describe this place. Little iron steps, landings, the wind whistles, one doesn't look down: knees are shaking. You climb upwards, as on a fire escape, and can't breathe because of the wind.

On the boom itself, above the precipice like a swallow's nest, is Sasha's booth, all glazed, full of air and sun. A soft revolving seat, levers, instruments, a "Moskvich" radio on a shelf covered by a white kerchief, a whole battery of little electric furnaces, and . . . a teapot wildly and merrily boiling on an ordinary stove.

Efremovich solemnly prepared the tea. He got three pot-bellied flowered cups from the little shelf, saucers, a little plate with butter, and a long loaf of raisin bread; he covered the high tension transformer with a newspaper, placed everything on it as on a table, lovingly, in exact symmetry, knocked up some sugar with little tongs, and invited us "to sit down."

I, as the guest of honor, was given the soft seat.

"Shall we listen to music?"

"Please."

"Just like the "Baikal" Restaurant. Fresh air and artistic landscapes!" Sasha said, turning on the receiver. "It's a lousy box, but receives everything because it almost reaches to the moon. We live as though in outer space. What are we listening to, Efremovich? India or Europe?

I didn't know whether to drink my tea or to admire. From the crane opened up a boundless view of the Angara, and the birds flew beneath our booth; the people below crept like ants. I merely stammered, but Sasha already had begun to describe his crane: he solemnly explained the principle of operation, the geometry of the bearing angles of the boom, and promised that we must climb up to the top platform, to the flag itself. He was proud of his machine; he was in love with it and awfully glad someone else also was interested in it.

When saying good-bye, I decided to put to them the same question I had asked Genka:

"Listen, I can't add on trips. Others worked here before I did; what did they do? Help!"

Sasha smiled thoughtfully and drummed his fingers on the handrails.

"Tolia, you're still quite naive. It's unpleasant to speak of such things. So what? They add on for us too. No, we don't depend on you. But if during the break we succeed in getting hold of a packet or two of fittings, that will line our pockets."

"This is an award for overtime work. It was used to buy the radio," Efremovich said edifyingly.

"But nonetheless it's lining your pocket, Efremovich?"

"Both of us still lack a communist consciousness. To make additions—is the evil of construction," said Efremovich. "They gnaw the soul of even the purest man like a worm. Were there angels here, they too would probably make additions. Man loves the kopeck. Even if not obtained by working."

"All this is so, Efremovich. But what should I do?"

"Give them the boot," Efremovich said resolutely.

Sasha burst out laughing, but I gave up and began to climb down. I had decided! On that very day I no longer gave a single excess trip. The "self-seeker with the gold teeth" destroyed me with a glance. Sorrowful 00-77 became more so. The next day I noticed that it was easier to work, there was no tension, and I was happier. But . . . I received seventy vehicles. Then—sixty. Then—forty.

They had run off! Assigned to our crane, some drivers made one or two trips for the sake of form and departed for other sectors where additions were made.

The brigade began to suffocate without concrete. Where is the concrete? Where is the concrete? Only I and the crane operators knew what the matter was. The vehicles queued up in the other sectors.

Genka the gypsy hauled as if nothing had happened and smiled his dazzling smile.

"Say, you don't line your pockets, so I've heard? Eccentric, that's too bad for you. What will be your percentage, have you thought of that? No, you'll add on, but not for nothing. Understand! You add on for him, and he'll do something for you: he'll take you home like a boss and bring you to work in the morning; you need firewood—firewood will be brought; gasoline, here it is! You have to know how to take advantage! And not make enemies."

Yes. So I had acquired my first enemies and strongly prejudiced the brigade . . . No, I don't understand anything. Is it impossible to remain honorable?

ALL FOR ONE

One of my duties is to close the tub when it returns empty from the block. On the first day Red Nikolai did this himself on the block, but the tub is swinging there, "walks", and is dangerous and difficult. On the bottom it has doors. Pull the lever, and the doors move. I began to do that from the second day.

"Y-you've become adept, so enough idling!" Nikolai "instructed" me.

But once something did happen which even now I remember with horror.

On that shift only we were pouring cement, and all the dump trucks, willingly or not, gathered at my place. Work was as crazy as on the first day. I threw myself at the lever, pressed with my entire body, slammed the doors, and yelled at the driver "Roll!" and at the crane operator "Lift!" I was excited and felt like singing.

I don't recall how I became confused, how I forgot about this lever: the crane snatched the next tub, lifted it above the viaduct . . . and suddenly the doors opened and the entire mass of many tons of concrete crashed down in such a terrible torrent from the tub onto the work bridge that thunder resounded and the handrail quivered. Fortunately, no one was nearby! After a "philosophical explanation" by Efremovich, I kept myself far back from the tub when the crane pulled it.

Sasha dangled the empty tub in the air—the residue fell out—and heavily banged it on the planking next to the mountain of concrete.

I clutched my head. Foremen came running, someone swore at the top of his voice, someone proved something to me . . . The concrete came in! How the concrete came in!

Because of me everything had come to a halt. The dump trucks honked, everyone tried to explain to me that one must close the doors, as if I didn't know myself! The concrete had blocked off half the passage, but the other half was unobstructed.

I closed the ill-starred lever and came to a decision: to press on with the concrete and leave this mountain alone. Cold sweat appeared on my forehead: if it hardens and sets, then a brigade with miners' picks will be required to remove it. And what will become of me!. . .

"Let's go, hurry up! Roll!"

I accepted two vehicles. The crane brought the tub. That's better already. Work resumed. While the vehicles are dumping, I'll shovel from the pile into the tub. But I tried just once and realized there was enough work for two days . . . I was ready to throw myself into this mountain and begin to sob, to drown in it. What was to be done?

And I worked for nearly an hour until orange circles started swimming before my eyes. You throw ten shovelfulls of this cast-iron weight and gasp for air, and the vehicles come in and in!

Someone's shovel began to scrape next to me. I turned and was dumbfounded. Tonia! Tonia with the falcon brows! Had she seen it and come? Quiet, smiling mysteriously, she didn't utter a single word. And I said nothing. Other girls appeared, talked as though nothing had happened, as though I weren't even there, as though this was their usual work.

"Take it from there. Where are you putting it?"

"From that edge. Dashka!"

"Gals! Ah my darlings!" Genka, the driver, rushed up, seized the shovel from my hands, and banging about like an excavator, began to shovel into the tub, his muscles flexing.

"You, my black-eyed gal! Step aside! Give room to a real workman. What are you looking at? Want to come along? Sit down in the booth, I'll give you a kiss!"

"Oh you, Gypsy, want me to take a stick to you?"

99

"Girls, seriously! Which of you will take me for a husband? Look, what a worker I am!"

"At the table, with a large spoon!"

Thus, with jokes and squeals, they removed more than half the mountain. I was initially disoriented, but then hurried on a vehicle and had it dump.

"Lif-t!"

Like bear-cubs they go thick and fast to the hole, to the stairs, in order to succeed in reaching the block while the crane is carrying the tub, and I nearly howled, for now I could finish it off myself, there would be no scolding!

Choosing a moment when there were no vehicles, Efremovich approached and stood next to me, hands in pockets.

"Sasha! Give me the tub. Lower. Hold the boom. More. Turn it."

I rushed toward the hanging tub so that when pouring it would be level. Efremovich stopped me:

"Don't do that. He can do it himself. A bit to the right. Swing round . . ."

I gaped. The tub turned lazily on the ropes, as though alive, settled, adjusted, and lay quietly with open mouth toward the concrete.

"Technology creates miracles," said Efremovich. "You must organize the work place so as to combine the useful with the agreeable."

He spat into his hands, took my shovel, and began to throw. Sasha flew headlong from the crane carrying a second shovel. They pushed me aside, stood side by side,—and on it crackled: khrr, khrr! I couldn't lift a hand, just stood and watched.

They, joking, scraped everything to the last drop, the boards sparkled as though they had been washed.

"Whew! Marvelous!" said Sasha. "You could throw like that all day, eh Efremovich?"

"I'd throw fat in my mouth all day," said Efremovich.

GLADIATORS IN A CAGE

Fatigue. Heavy, cheerless fatigue, like incessant rain. Wherever I am, whatever I do, it hammers: rest, rest. Besides everything else, my money is running out; fifteen rubles are left, and one three-ruble note is torn and somehow must be glued together. It's a long time until an advance of wages. When I'm too tired to be hungry, I don't have supper.

Either Moskalenko guessed why they were transporting so little concrete to us, or she said simply by chance:

"We work in turns at the reception area in order to rest. The time has come for you to do some real work, in the block."

And I transferred to the block.

Do you know, have you ever thought about, how concrete workers work? The block is an enormous box knocked together out of boards. Everything inside is partitioned and tangled up by reinforcement rods. The concrete is poured from above. The concrete workers crawl about inside, drowning up to their knees in the dirty liquid mash, spreading the pile with shovels and tamping it with tampers. The entire box must be filled up to the top. The tamper weighs one and a half poods,* and poods of concrete on your feet too. Like gladiators in an ancient Roman circus—down below, within walls, in a cage.

"Mashka, where are you throwing! Oh you so-and-so, cow. Tamp!"

"The tamper doesn't work."

"Electrician! Electrician, where the deuce are you! . . ."

From the electrician's booth comes Pet'ka the photographer, clambering apelike along the steel reinforcement: he is on duty with our brigade. He gets pliers, turns the wires, makes sparks.

* (Russian measure of weight equal to 16.8 kilograms or about 36 pounds—transl.)

A tamper resembles somewhat a miner's pick. It doesn't have a chisel at the end, but a small heavy cylinder with a tiny motor inside. You push a button—the tamper begins to shake so much that it jumps out of your hands. The shaking cylinder plunges into the viscous mass of cement—and on it goes! The concrete bubbles, floats, and thickens. This is called "tamping." This must be done along all the concrete, layer by layer, otherwise cavities will remain (a defect for which the technical inspectorate does not pat one on the back).

This is highly complex and responsible work, difficult also because it is monotonous. To become a tamper one must complete a course, but in these hectic days they accepted me and allowed me to tamp because I had taken physics in a ten-grade school and was required to know the principle of vibration and in general to comprehend the chemistry of the concrete process and be quick on the uptake. "Educated"—climb into the baskets and don't pretend about anything.

I lasted for two shifts. After the third I took to my bed. My hands shook like a paralytic, the mad tamper seemed to pull my joints apart. The team leader, Dasha, rested her hands on the side, observed how I fought the tamper when trying to extract it from the viscous mass, spat and swore:

"Well, what a worker they sent us! You so-and-so, crawl out on the steel reinforcement, take a rest, and you'll open the tub."

Dashka can't tolerate the use of foul language. But she herself loves to swear. Therefore she has a "substitute": you so-and-so.

To open the tub is "intellectual" labor. One requires brains and dexterity. The cages are above the reinforcement at the height of a three-storey house. There are breezes there, a few reinforcements sag and swing under foot with a light clink. On your hands and knees you catch hold of the shaking rods and think: how am I going to straighten up?

Above, in the blue sky, the tub looms, flying purposively, scattering crushed stone and dripping mortar.

"Girls! Step aside!"

They rush to the walls. Sasha Gurzii smiles from his remote booth and carefully lowers the tub toward me. I wave my hand: lower, a bit more, mind the boom. Stop!

Crawling apelike toward the tub, I get hold of it and straighten up. It slowly "walks", the damned shark, on the ropes, turns. I press against it with all my strength, lead it, level it. Now I must pull a rope and get cracking—like a cannon. I crawl back . . . lean backwards as far as possible . . . Pull! Pull!

It doesn't work. I set my feet better. Pull! Pull!

I turn red, my feet slip, knees shake. Jerk, and jerk again!

"Harder, you so-and-so! We don't have to pave the way for you, do we?"

I gather my remaining strength. Either I'll collapse or I'll open it. Pull!

Like a gunshot the levers start working: "Gur-dur-gur-r-bakh-trakh!" The concrete pours like an avalanche into the block, the tub jumped up, the reinforcement settled, and I grabbed on to the rods and began to shake, like a sparrow on a branch, neither dead nor alive.

"Fi-ne! Go-o-on!"

I look, Sasha Gurzii clasps his hands above his head and reassures me: everything is fine. The ropes quivered, the tub flew up. That's the first! . . . Well, no better or worse than the others . . . I wiped the cold sweat from my brow.

That's how we work.

WHO ARE THEY?

It's me who is so weak and helpless. It's for me that there are so many fears and hardships. Our concrete workers are stronger than I am, they work as though they are digging a kitchen-garden or cutting timber—measuredly, making jokes, without strain. They would have to have been made of steel, if they were not ordinary girls.

TONIA WITH THE FALCON BROWS. There are two Tonias in the world: one at dances, and the other at the block. Here she is taciturn and economical in her movements; she works only with the tamper and in the most important places: the corners, along the walls, among especially complex reinforcement interlacing. Dasha respects her very much and never swears at her. In Tonia's place I would already have expired.

"How can you be on the tamper all the time?!"

"It listens to me. I don't even strain myself: it goes by itself, I only guide it."

"But you pull it out?"

"Well, physical exercise is useful! Try to do it as I do. It's alive, it has character! Have a try, there's no tub yet . . ."

Tonia differs from the others in that she is slender and elegant—yes, yes, elegant!—even in those bear-like overalls and rubber boots. I don't know how this is achieved. Other girls look like sacks or bears, but she's slender, the overalls fit her as though she were poured into them, a watch gleams on her arm. She's also less dirty and her hands less disfigured . . .

Sometimes she raises her flushed face, her hair coming out from under her kerchief, and looks at the sky from the bottom of the cage. Our glances meet, I want to straighten up and rakishly adjust my forelock, but she looks serious, as though mysteriously asking something. Then she smiles in a friendly manner and bends down again.

Those glances are our secret. No one notices them. Tonia also doesn't suspect how much they attract me . . .

VALIA SEREDA. She's a native of Bodaibo. An unwed mother. Snubnosed, high cheek-bones, compact, and nice! I have never seen her frown, be irritable, or quarrel with anyone. Entangled in wires, drowning in concrete, her boots filled with mortar, pulling the tamper with all her strength, she chatters down below:

"Oh, girls! Today my Vovka said: 'Mama! In the circus the clown is the most important of all. When I grow up, I'll become a clown too!' "

She chatters and chatters about various trivialities but it doesn't get on one's nerves; on the contrary, it seems were she to leave, the block would be empty.

104

"Girls! I almost forgot: cucumbers have arrived in our store, fine, slightly salted, delicious! Get them quickly, while they're available. I can get them, who wants some?"

She loves to sing. Our best singer. Either during the break and even at work, she leads with her melodious ringing voice, and the others pick it up, slowly, moving in rows with their tampers from wall to wall and singing . . .

TASIA, THE LITTLE BEAR. She is tiny, kind, and pretty, except for her hands—huge, red laboring hands. Wrapped up and bound, she's round like a ball and even her face is covered by a shawl so it doesn't peel. Recently she married the driver of an earth-moving machine.

From time to time Tasia, panting in a business-like manner, clambers along the reinforcement to the wall and, shading her eyes from the sun with her hand, looks around: where in the distance, on the dam, is her husband's earth-moving machine? She sees it, beams, and plops back into the concrete.

Sometimes chaos breaks out at the block:

"Tasia! Tasia! Come quickly! Tolia has come!"

That means Tolia had come by in his earth-moving machine and jumped down for a second. Well-built and blond, he's smeared all over with grease and smells of solidole; he stands on the stairs and smiles. Tasia rolls toward him like a ball, they hold hands, and stand and gaze into one another's eyes.

Whether there is urgent work or not, even Dashka the Snake releases Tasia for three minutes, albeit grumbling:

"Go, you so-and-so, go on, kiss your Tolia!"

DASHKA, THE SNAKE. Our team leader is the most ill-tempered and loudest of the girls. She is plump and strong as iron. She's under twenty years of age. Freckled face, yellow teeth, earrings in her ears—exactly the same as some village wench. But she has taken courses and worked as a tractor driver and bricklayer, has built houses in Moscow on Leschanai Street, and was at the Stalingrad Hydroelectric Station. She's a virago—and my nemesis. Not a second does she give me to rest, never a kind word nor a friendly glance. Sometimes I'm ready to loathe her.

"Tol'ka-a! You so-and-so, pick up the pencil, calculate the volume of this heap. Quickly! What did they teach you in school?"

She apparently is angry with me because I have a secondary education and she does not. We hunt for cubes—to place more and more. We count, calculate, compute. I feverishly try to recall: height, 6: pir^2 . . . 3.1416 to multiply with.

Dasha is fidgety, checks me, finds a mistake made in the hurry, and sarcastically calls me a docent, professor, or academician, depending on the extent of the divergence.

RED NIKOLAI. There are few men in the brigade, in our team only Nikolai and myself. They say that many men have been in the Moskalenko Brigade, but some left of their own volition and she drove away the others. Moskalenko prefers girls, and some of them have been working with her for four years.

I don't know why she keeps Nikolai. He's a genuine red devil: coarse, ill-tempered, morose, lazy—I can not describe him otherwise. Nikolai is a misogynist. His wife never talks at home, merely "hisses," and he calls the girls "peasant girls." In return they insult him as they please.

The fact is that Nikolai tries to use every free minute to lie down. He finds himself some sort of hole among the blocks, brings paper and boards with nails and iron pieces, and every free second he's there, lying down.

"Look, Kolia's already found a hen-house!" the girls laugh. "Kolia! Ko-ko-ko! Kud-ku-da! Laid an egg? Ko-ko-ko! . . ."

Only Nikolai's blue nose protruded from the "hen-house" and from time to time clouds of smoke puff. He doesn't deign to answer.

"The tub-b!"

Nikolai leaps up—and crawls on all fours along the steel reinforcement like a spider out of ambush: jumps, gallops—catches, and balances. Pull! The concrete is still pouring down, but he sidles, crawls to the hen-house, and lies down!

Now he and I are neighbors, we are pouring into adjacent sluices. I watch attentively and can't understand it: I work very hard, stay on the reinforcement, don't leave for a second, bake in the sun, boil, but Nikolai pours more concrete. What's the explanation?

Thus did the days pass. Now I'm already "at home" in the foundation ditch. I run to drink some water at Pet'ka the photographer's booth. He has iron, wires, light bulbs, and amperemeters there, and he, like Pliushkin, loves to rummage about in his treasures, he repairs tampers, connects up spotlights, and still succeeds in photographing. His dream is to create a photographic record of the construction site.

I encounter Zakhar Zakharych: he's transporting crushed stone to our block and always waves from the cab in greeting. We all feel at home here in the foundation ditch.

Our guests are tourists from Irkutsk, various types, school children. They stare, wander about the cranes, understand nothing, rush about among the vehicles. I pass by with a slow, careless gait, paying no attention to them . . . When they stand as a scared lot on the viaduct and watch how we are working, even idle Nikolai doesn't crawl into the "hen house." We are on view, we represent sent the brigade, and we know that the foreman who from boredom is a tourist guide is now going to explain: "This is the Moskalenko Brigade, they have the banner, it's the very best brigade." It's astonishing how much the construction site foremen know, they explain the entire technology to you!

And there's no getting rid of the correspondents. They represent all kinds of newspapers—and each seeks people from his own home-town, and they must be outstanding workers. And who of us is an outstanding worker? How to distinguish him? The day before yesterday a correspondent from Moscow photographed the entire brigade. He ordered us to clean up and pose; for his sake we kept the tub suspended for half an hour, became "dynamic," that is, stand as we never do since it is contrary to all technical safety rules and methods. He snapped ten times and, satisfied, left, and we clambered again into our cage.

107

THE SO-AND-SO

So, there's no money left, if you don't take account of the torn three-ruble note. What shall I do? I'm completely confused and don't know how all
this will end.

During each lunch break we send someone to the canteen for kvass and
sandwiches. We pool our resources and eat lunch—or, more accurately,
"drink lunch" because of terrible thirst.

Today, Dasha, as usual, approached me for money. I was ashamed to
give her the torn three-ruble note.

"Hey, you so-and-so, do you expect a special invitation?"

"I don't want anything today."

"Oh, you!" She gave me such a contemptuous glance and looked me
over from head to toe that I wanted to strike her, to slap her one, so that she
. . . Easy. Don't be irritated.

They all sat down in the shade, on the sluice-gate, talking happily about
something else, and I decided for no reason in particular to clean the steel reinforcement: everyone would have less work at the end of the shift.

It was very hot and I wanted to drink. I hack and chop with my shovel
along the rods, scrape. Then Red Nikolai came crawling along the steel reinforcement on all fours. He pretended that he was crawling for some reason of
his own, but approached closer and closer, awkwardly, like a bear. I tensed
and was on the alert.

"What are you doing," he said gloomily. "Give me a Belomor."

"They're all gone . . ." I muttered. I had in fact run out of cigarettes.

"I see. No money?"

"I have money."

"Nonsense," he concluded calmly and reached into his pocket. "There,
take it."

He held out a 25-ruble note.

"Well, take it, Pay it back from your cash advance. My wife told me to buy an oil-cloth with it. Take it, I said!" he began to yell crossly and threateningly.

"A . . . a . . . your wife isn't going to hiss at you?"

"W-well, l-let her."

He left awkwardly along the steel reinforcement as he had come, and I was left alone, dumbstruck, with the money in my fist.

Not five minutes had elapsed, when:

"Tol'ka-a-a! Come here, you so-and so!"

Again it begins, again Dashka. Heavens, what did I do to displease her?

"Tol'ka-a-a!"

"I'm coming. Well, I'm coming."

"Oh, you fine gentleman! I've got to crawl out to you, do I? Get down here at once!"

I jumped, flopped down onto the soft concrete, and stood facing her. Dashka suddenly lowered her voice, slipped something to me, and whispered:

"Here, silly. The girls have made a collection. 100 rubles. Keep you going. If it's not enough, we'll find more."

She embarrassedly thrust again and again at me the three- and one-ruble notes, flushing with vexation. She began to yell:

"Still sniveling! Lout! You so-and-so, no more tricks! 'I don't want!' Look at the fine gentleman. Forward march to the sluice-gate! Everything there in the bucket and paper is yours. Quick, while they aren't sending concrete in. Well?!"

Obeying her automatically, I submissively shuffled over to the sluice-gate. The girls were seated on the opposite wall, laughing, telling anecdotes, and then someone brought a newspaper and they began to read. Nobody paid any attention to me. On the sluice-gate stood a bucket of kvass, a glass next to it, and on the paper two rolls with cheese slices.

"OH, MY SHIP PLIES THE BLUE SEA"

Where is life taking me? Where will it deposit me? Will I be a worker, condemned to founder about in concrete, while Vic becomes a supply agent and owner of his own dacha? What is Siberia? Misfortune or good luck? . . . no, good luck is not to be seen, rather it is misfortune . . .

We are seated on the top of a nearly completed waste-gate and "are relaxing" in the absence of concrete. Now it's night.

The brigade has been transferred to the third shift, after twelve. For whoever doesn't know what the third shift is, it's better not to know.

At 3:00 a.m. you begin to nod off to sleep. Arms and legs feel like cotton, eyelids droop. Oh, to lie down, to curl up! You understand nothing: what to do or why? It's cold: the Siberian nights are frosty, with hoar-frost in the morning. At first you're hot, but at dawn your teeth are chattering.

Today we finished the waste-gate; the girls smoothed the slopes with their hands. These are the most renowned waste-gates which figure in pictures when they want to portray the hydroelectric station, Yes, they smoothed them by hand from bottom to top, the entire sloping wall, like a coagulated waterfall. Simple and commonplace: Dasha is seated, near her a bucket of muddy water, a little board, a trowel—and she spreads, conveys, smooths, like peasant women in the village polish a stove. To look down from the top is terrifying: if you slip and slide downwards, you can't stop yourself.

At first the work was hellish, a madhouse: the concrete plant was trying to set a record. We were sinking in concrete, the vehicles had bunched up, the drivers were honking, we didn't get on with tamping or smoothing; the entire waste-gate grew thus, straight to the top. And now we sit and freeze: the concrete mixer at the plant had broken down, without having broken the record.

Nikolai has crawled into the "hen-house," the girls clasp one another closely, look at the stars, and are singing. The song is melancholy, long drawn-out, the voices meld together, then some go higher, others lower . . .

110

Oh, on the blue sea
My ship sails.
Oh, the ship sails,
And the waves roar . . .

For some reason it's very quiet today. The song doubtless is audible throughout the construction site. The spotlights are buzzing, moths flitting around them. I also want to clasp everyone, to lie down, place my head on someone's knees. I close my eyes and ships appear. Waves roar and splash on the waste-gate, seething white-caps. It's fresh! Windy! Spray! The sea, it's our sea. And the ships are plying the sea, with scarlet sails . . .

I open my eyes: the moths are flitting around the lights, the girls have bunched into a dark pile, hands in their sleeves, steam coming out of their mouths, and someone relates in a frightened whisper:

". . . Old Baikal boiled up, raised himself on his bed, seized an enormous mountain in his fury and hurled it after an unruly daughter. The mountain fell on the daughter's turquoise veil—there, where the cliffs parted but did not restrain the unrestricted run of the Angara.

Since then 335 obedient rivers flow into Baikal, and the unruly Angara alone carries out everything that they bring in . . ."

I felt shaky and stuffy. I went along to the neighboring block, leaned with my back against the wooden beam, listened to new songs from afar, how Moskalenko sings in Ukrainian—she's a Ukrainian from Dneprostroi—and admired the sunrise.

Noiselessly, swiftly, the sky was set aflame, at first it was cold and grey, then pink arrows and stripes of clouds, next a whole fire started. The Angara was visible to me, curved dragon-like, smooth and integral, like a mirror, and it flowed toward the remote and wild North . . .

Beyond earshot:

111

"The cockerel crowed long ago, children, get ready for school! Oh, a shower. Oh, good!"

I feel as though someone is throwing handfuls of sand at me. I open my eyes, the sun and rain are directly in my face!

I leapt up, grabbed crazily at the beam, and around me people were clapping their hands and laughing. Already it's a clear, bright, cloudless day. It's warm, the sun gives warmth all over. Valia and Tonia are watering the waste-gate with a hose. That damned prankster Val'ka has aimed the jet directly at me.

"Val'ka, stop it! Va-a-a . . . I'll kill you!"

She is choking with laughter. Well, what's one to do: my entire overalls are as though after a rain. She found some amusement! Very funny!

"It's nearly 8.00 a.m., get up, lazybones. We had finished work. I'll tell my Vovka: today your mama listened to stones. Ga-als! Yesterday Vovka asked me: 'Mama! Will there be communism soon?' "

"Well, surely, that's not true!"

"I swear it is!"

The girls clean the shovels and make ready. Dasha thoughtfully and thoroughly spreads the tarpaulins along the wet concrete of the waste-gate: it will be a hot day. So that our unhardened concrete won't crack.

"Tonia," I said, "Squirt me with the hose."

She tilts the hose, and I, having rolled down my overalls to my waist, have a shower-bath in the cold, bracing stream of water. The showers take my breath away. I bathe and bathe and want still more. Tonia waits patiently, smiling a little.

"All right?"

"Oh, fine! You girls don't know this delight: to shower-bathe to the waist—it's like being reborn, br-r! . . . Poor you."

"That's so?"

"Tonia . . ."

"Huh?"

". . . Is that true?"

She is silent, looks at me with her pensive blue eyes; the hose shakes and hums in her hands.

"Tonia, aren't you sorry for your hands? Look what's happened to them."

"I'm sorry. Don't look at them! Go help Dasha. She's completely entangled."

I go, pull the tarpaulins, crawl, smooth out the corners.

If you only knew, Tonia, how I myself have become entangled! . . .

WE GATHERED VIOLETS

The money, of course, I didn't retain. My remarkable Len'ka also hadn't managed well and . . . he came to ask for a loan from me. I honestly gave him half of it.

"Well, then let's go fishing," he said. "As always: when you're short, you go catch Gobius.*"

We left in the morning and went far up the Angara. From the hills we saw below, as if it were on a map, our little town and the construction site, and a half-dozen gantry cranes, of which the farthest away was mine . . .

We went farther and farther. The forest became denser, higher, the little paths disappeared, we left the kitchen-gardens behind, and we moved straight ahead, forcing our way through the dry undergrowth, which snapped in our hand like macaroni, with a crackling sound and rising dust, and the cobwebs clung to our faces and hair, fell into our eyes—we had to hold our hands outstretched so that they stuck to our sleeves instead.

Good Lord, how many flowers there were! Enormous ones, like glasses, tiny ones, like beads . . . fiery red, violet wild rosemary, red, blue, pink, they seemed unreal! Thickets of ferns covered the terraced slopes, and among the

* (a small fish found in the Black Sea and the Lake Baikal—transl.)

rocks protruded fragile, cold and delicate, tulips. There was the aroma of hot grass, it was easy and sweet to breath, and one wanted to fall into the grass, into the network of sun-spots, closing one's eyes and lying there, listening to the buzzing of the flies and the noise of little spiders.

Everything around was so full of life, so harmonious—wise, eternal, wild . . .

"Chiu-vi-it'!" A thin penetrating whistle rang out right next to us. On the trunk of a pine, spread like a squirrel, sat a tiny striped animal looking at us out of his shiny eyes with curiosity.

"Ah, my dear, my little fool!" Len'ka had stopped, quite touched, and was as happy as though he had seen a friend. "Oh, my little chipmunk! How's life? How are things in general? Why are you hiding?"

The chipmunk squeaked weakly and darted to the other side of the trunk. We stood still. First its eyes appeared, then its tiny forehead, and its most curious little eyes stared—like children peering round a corner when playing hide-and-seek.

Len'ka became excited, like a child. He tenderly patted the tree, picked flowers, hummed, and began to relate how he and his father had lived in a winter hut—a winter hut is simply a little hut in the taiga, a farm. Len'ka had owned a remarkable dog named Val'va, and she had smelled wood-grouse far off.

"So you go through the forest. But it, the cunning little bird, sat on a tree somewhere and slept. Val'va sniffs for a moment—barks, jumps against the tree, goes mad, but he, the fool, struts, sits closer down, and watches with one eye. He hears nothing! He's terribly interested: what sort of animal is that? . . . It falls like an old larch tree! Bang—the entire forest moans, stirs for a long time: 'A tree has died . . .' "

Len'ka's eyes were shining, and he talked and talked, jumped over rocks, chatted with the birds, to a beetle, as though he were a guest who for a long time hadn't managed to get away but had come, and had forgotten no one, and for every one had saved a kind word.

"Just wait, brother, we'll come together a bit later. There's a red whortleberry, see it, still green. But then we'll gorge ourselves here. And raspberries! Great bilberries there will be too! Then we'll put all our pay packet in the savings bank, you'll see! We'll gather nuts, oh, what nuts there are!"

Having cut ten fishing rods, we descended to the Angara.

No matter how often I see the Angara, I can't get used to it. It rushes like a tram, like a hawk diving from the sky, but quietly, without rapids and noise, only the surface bubbles intensely and forms whirlpools . . . It is astonishingly quiet, one hears little stones rustle on the riverbed, and before your eyes runs the turquoise water, pure as a tear.

Face to face with this peaceful impetuous miracle, I comprehend simply and clearly how the legend was born of the proud and audacious escape of Angara. I look and feel dizzy, it seems I'm dreaming.

Len'ka cast his lines and propped them up with stones.

"Does this mean we'll go for a swim?"

"I'm scared . . ."

"Nonsense! I've swum the Enisei—five kilometers—man, I'm telling you!"

I plucked up my courage and, with a running start, plunged into the water. At first it seemed I was immersed in boiling water. It took my breath away, I opened my mouth but couldn't cry out. The current carried me away like a straw. Floundering with my remaining strength, I crawled like a dog onto the pebbles and only there gasped the air. But Len'ka stood chest-deep in the water, patting himself on the shoulders, and laughed:

"It bites, doesn't it? Fine! Fast! Marvelous! Aha-a!"

He was diving like a seal, snorting, gurgling, in perfect bliss. I returned to the shore, to our clothes, then tried once again to enter ankle-deep. My feet ached as though I were on ice, every bone ached. This was all the more surprising since from above the sun was very hot, and the pebbles on the shore were as hot as coals. I jumped out.

"You'll get used to it." Len'ka tried to persuade me. He had swum out to great depths. "Get used to it, this is your Siberia!"

Once more I plunged in, sat in the water for ten seconds, and rushed to the shore with a disgraceful howl. My teeth were chattering.

Len'ka came in content and red, and consoled me condescendingly:

"You'll get used to it. When I swam across the Enisei, I too lay on the stove for two days."

No. I shan't swim the Enisei . . . But why am I so puny, why on earth was I born and raised in the city? Oh! . . . And I once even had imagined myself to be strong. So many times I had taken first place in school races!

My mood became gloomy, suddenly for some reason I felt nauseous. Recently I have felt sick rather often. And that's not surprising: you eat what can be found, whenever there's a moment, and you get very tired.

The floats of all ten fishing lines had gone down, probably they were soaked through. But Len'ka clicked his teeth.

"O.K.! They're hooked."

He approached the fishing rods and quietly pulled out in turn ten Gobius, red, tadpole-like; the smallest was the size of a finger, the largest of a palm. I gasped with amazement.

"Other fish gulp the hook, run, jump, fight," Len'ka explained while baiting the hooks. "But the Gobius—is a fellow with a large head; he takes the hook and sits quietly. He knows: he's been caught. We'll do as follows: I'll cast and you'll haul them in. They're already queuing out there."

I didn't believe my eyes. Len'ka went forward, cast the lines, and placed the rods on the water. I picked them up immediately, pulled—and unhooked a Gobius. This was incredible. After the first hundred, this monotonous unbelievable angling simply turned into mechanical work. We pulled and pulled—like radishes in the kitchen-garden.

We ate fish soup until satiated, and then slept on the hot rocks.

I awakened first. Already it was becoming cool. Len'ka was sweetly snoring, broad-chested, sinewy, like the Hercules in the Pushkin Museum. It was quiet as before, the stones rustled, and the Angara like a noiseless mirage sped by.

In the distance, through the haze, I only now noticed the tiny silhouettes

116

of the six gantry cranes; the farthest being mine . . . A dot, a small island, five kopeck's worth of culture in this untouched, wild world. And I was brought here. Could I stand it?

Again I felt ill. I remembered the fish soup and felt loathing: in it swam boiled heads and fins, but we had gulped them down, crunched the heads. I needn't have eaten so much. Yes, I had taken first place in the competitions in school, but here it turns out that I'm simply a kid. You could give Len'ka a gun and a rusty hook and let him loose for a year or two in the taiga—and he would live like a piece of cake, nothing frightens him; to him the world is like home, and the construction site, a plaything. But I . . .

The sun was setting, and the Angara was shot through with violet, green, gold. Huge fish played, jumping here and there. Above the hills the evening clouds had opened their fiery wings. And the more beautiful it became, the more alarming became my thoughts.

"Len'ka, get up, let's go home!"

"What's the matter with you?"

"Nothing. Let's go home."

"You look awful! What happened?"

"Oh, nothing. Feeling sick . . ."

"Well-l . . . Ate too much fish soup. Wait a bit, we'll catch more Gobius and then go."

"I don't want any more Gobius. Let's go at once!" I said this in such an unexpectedly capricious tone that I myself felt ashamed, but Len'ka looked blank.

We went across the meadow toward the hills. Myriads of violets were growing on this meadow. I was feverish, nauseous, and suddenly a strange colic in the stomach bent me double.

"What?" Len'ka asked.

"Let's pick violets . . ."

"For the girls? Yes?" Len'ka was delighted. "A fine idea!"

He, suspecting nothing, picked whole bundles of violets. Violet circles swam before my eyes, but I kept on. We went on slowly and at sunset reached

117

the slope. Here a new bout of pain and nausea forced me to throw my bouquet away and sit down on a rock.

Len'ka was frightened, began to bustle about, said something, but I yelled:

"Go ahead! I'll rest. Go ahead, I said!"

He tactfully went on ahead, climbed the slope, for a moment his silhouette with the fishing rods loomed against the darkening sky, and then disappeared.

I, near collapse, entirely covered in a cold sweat, rested a bit, and crawled after him. Len'ka was sitting in the grass, waiting for me. From here opened, as from a gantry crane, a boundless view of the silvery ribbon of the Angara, the evening distant prospect, the hills covered by the taiga.

"Len'ka, Len'ka!" I said, choking. "Get me some money! I'll return to Moscow. I'll send it back to you from there, I swear it, word of honor!"

"Oh, you!" Len'ka whispered. "What's the matter with you? Tolia, what's with you?"

"Get me some money, I ask you, I implore you! I'll return today, at once, I can't take any more, I can't! I want to go home!"

"Well, well, stop it. Calm down! It's the Gobius . . ."

"Throw them away, I can't look at them!"

He looked at me and obediently threw a bunch of the Gobius into the grass.

"Len'ka, I need some money! Len'ka, Lenechka, my dear! Two hundred rubles for an ordinary ticket, otherwise I'll run on foot. I'm no good here, I'll perish. To hell with it, to hell! Two hundred rubles!"

Len'ka clasped my shoulders tenderly and awkwardly.

"Tolia, my dear! . . . There is no money . . . None."

He continued:

"There's no money. No one has any. It can't be obtained . . . Bear up. Get control of yourself. Oh you, Good Lord! Hang on, control yourself. Understand? You feel bad, but try. Well, swear at me; listen, if you wish—strike me, go ahead, well, go ahead. Don't be afraid, I don't mind!"

He really didn't know how to behave, what to say to me, a capricious, spoiled child, how to counter such a whim.

"Try to understand: it is possible to leave. You'll receive a cash advance, to the train station, and home. Only if you indulge yourself once—all your life indulgences will go on, you'll be given up for lost! We'd best go home, get hold of yourself. Oh, you shouldn't have eaten those Gobius! Let's go! . . . You'll earn some money, take some leave, travel. You wish us to do it together? I shan't! Well, for you the world is big enough just in Moscow!"

I didn't listen attentively to what else he said. The illness had passed on a bit. I got up, found the Gobius in the grass, silently passed the bunch to Len'ka, took half of the fishing rods from him, and, biting my lips, went on.

Leonid gave me half of his violets, and we placed two bouquets under the door at No. 4, Primorskaia, quietly, having slipped into the corridor like thieves.

AN ANXIOUS NIGHT

On this night I went to work slowly and painfully. For the first time I was absolutely indifferent to what I was doing and how, I only wanted the shift to be over as quickly as possible.

Imagine mountains of turned earth, littered with chips and beams, and in the midst of this a high inclining wooden wall. Within it's empty, we are pouring concrete there. After the waste-gate we are building a shore embankment, a quay. On one side it will be square, and on the other—the waters will seethe, shooting out of the station turbines. No, it's not an empty wall; of course, it's full of steel reinforcement. It's very tight in there, overalls get caught on hooks, there's no place to turn around, the cords of the tampers are entangled, the light from the spotlights is inadequate.

Nikolai opens the tub from above and pours, and I accept vehicles below the crane. The gantry doesn't reach there, so they brought in a steam "Shkoda." It is incomprehensible how it crawled there on its wide, worn, and twisted caterpillar tracks across the mountains of earth. It's like a two-storey house, sprinkled with coal dust all over, and it puffs like a locomotive. It's dark, burning cinders, are emitted from the furnace; the operators look out of it, then hide in the cab, smudgy, preoccupied; somewhere not far away a bulldozer squeaks, and from time to time sparks shoot out from the crane's funnel with a bang.

It's cool. I'm shivering and sick.

I long for something. Something I lack. But what it is I don't know myself; it merely seems that should I be able to get it a load would be removed from me, and the world would be an easier and happier place to live in. But what was it? Or am I ill?

My old acquaintance with the melancholy eyes, the driver of vehicle 00-77, was the first to bring concrete. I was glad to see him, and he spoke to me for the first time, said it was difficult to reach us.

Oh, the drivers at construction sites! You drive your worn out, hard working vehicles over all kinds of holes, mounds, impassable mud, and ruts! Your dump trucks are in such terrible shape they wouldn't even be admitted to the suburbs of Moscow. But you manage to do 100,000 kilometers without major repairs, wear the rubber to the last little shred, and still try to economize. To come to us here—the devil himself would break his leg, but 00-77 came, the concrete didn't spill, and he merely noted that it was difficult to reach us.

The "self-seeker with the golden teeth" arrived second—half the concrete had spilled en route.

"Ho! Friends meet again!" He greeted me joyfully, not leaving the cab. "How's your pencil doing today?"

"Not bad!"

"But the work doesn't go well today . . . It's legal if you give me a couple of crosses, isn't it?"

Truly the work wasn't going well. Nikolai couldn't put the tubs into the narrow funnel-shaped opening of the wall. The crane operator swore, was afraid the heavy tub might break away from the boom. The crane puffed

120

heavily, tugged, clanked. But in the narrow wooden cage the girls removed the cables so the concrete wasn't poured on them, pressed into the corners of the walls, and covered themselves. And then: grr-bukh-bukh-shlep-trakh! Poured!

A howling begins in the block:

"Who the devil asked you to pour it? Kol'ka-a-a-a! You parasite! Now come and throw it in the proper place yourself!"

"O.K. Shut up!" Nikolai says with dignity into the hole and sits down to have a smoke. "P-peasants! Your concern is slight: you only know how to tamp!"

He walks warily on the block, grabs the pintles, waves his arms, and against the background of the stars looks like a lonely and muddle-headed hen which can't find its roost.

Finally they ceased transporting concrete completely.

Nikolai descended from the wall down the stairway, gathered a pile of chips, dragged a pail from under the pitch, and a large beam crushed by an excavator, threw it all down in a heap and set it afire.

"Wonderful! A bonfire—a first priority. Eh, girls! . . ."

Dasha managed to get out of the block, covered from head to toe in concrete, came over, sat down, turned sideways toward the fire and joyously narrowed her eyes, nice, kind, as though she had not abused Nikolai just a moment ago.

"In the winter, Anatolii, it's so cold—whew!" said Nikolai. "I'm on the viaduct, in the wind. The peasant women are in the block, but on the viaduct—a blizzard, my death. How to save myself? I gather chips and light them in an empty tub. There is iron around, it doesn't burn. I crawl into the tub, inhale the smoke—oh, how pleasant!"

"Tell about the fireman," Dasha said.

"Well, when the bosses come along, I trample it underfoot at once and pour some water over it, as though it weren't I. Whence the smoke? I've been smoking. Once a fireman caught me. I hadn't recognized him: there was a very strong blizzard. Oh, how he went for me! 'You so-and-so,' he said, 'you'll burn down the Irkutsk Hydroelectric Station!' I insisted: 'How can I save myself?'—He said 'I'll save you!' He ran off to look for the sector head. I quickly extinguished the fire, threw the ashes below, put snow on the spot, and went off myself. I clambered up to Efremovich's gantry and watched. They came, walked round and round . . . And I observed. The boss said: 'It can't be, I know Nikolai, he wouldn't do it.' So they went away. Later I encountered the boss. 'You,' he said, 'may make a fire, but so the firemen don't see.' O.K. We know. What of summer? Plenty."

Not far away lay a coal box. I turned it toward the fire, lay a board onto it, and stretched out. The iron was like ice, the bonfire had gone out. Sometimes a rumble aroused me, I leapt up, ran outside to the vehicle, but there was no vehicle; the crane's boiler was rumbling and gurgling. In a dream I saw the winter: Moscow was piled high with snow, and along Gor'kii Street passes a column of snow-removal men. The thermometer at the Moscow Soviet shows minus 35 degrees centigrade. But I, a schoolboy, briefcase in hand, walk on and chew a tangerine, its yellow peels left on the snow. New Year's day is soon, we have a cultural excursion to see "The Nutcracker." . . .

The "self-seeker" awakened me; he had brought a cubic meter of concrete which he had "milked" from the plant and said that there was a breakdown and there will be no concrete for some time. I shivered with cold, felt as though I were drunk—perhaps I was ill, or maybe sleepy.

"Well, listen, lad," this strong man began to pester, "add five trips. You see yourself what kind of work this is. Well, wouldn't I gladly haul more? I've extracted a cubic meter . . . Well, add on a bit, I beg you, for my children's milk. I have several, and they all squeak: Give, give, give me!"

I got out my pad and jotted down three trips for him. Later I felt sorry for the driver of "00-77" and added two for him.

"There, for this let's go warm up at the crane!" said the driver happily, taking me by the hand.

We clambered on to the crane, opened the iron door, and . . . there was a blast of warmth, a fire from the open furnace door. The stoker, black like a miner, grinned:

"What-t? You've come? Why the deuce don't you drop in during the day . . ."

"Gosh! Paradise, a marvelous life!" the "self-seeker" exclaimed spiritedly. "If there were a fair-haired maiden here, you could live forever. Friend, bring some water."

The stoker dived into the darkness, behind odd mechanisms, cylinders, pressure gauges, brought a pail with soot swimming in it, and we drank with pleasure.

"Crawl over to the sleeping-bench," the stoker said. "Zhorka's sleeping there, you make room but don't wake him."

Having climbed on to the ladder below the roof, we found ourselves on some sort of platform of boards, and on it lay jerseys, trousers, and rags. Next to them in the darkness lay a scorching pipe, it was hot, like a steamhouse. My entire body relaxed at once in a sweet lassitude.

I dreamed about Komsomol'skaia Square in Moscow. I'm rushing to the tram station. Hot. Stuffy. The Muscovites are rushing to the dacha trains. All are completely packed; the electric trains depart one after another. Ice cream sells like hot cakes. I'm very happy: now we're going to the forest, the river, fishing. Oh, those Gobius. Didn't you know that Len'ka and I set a world record for catching fish on rusty hooks! Only I feel a bit ill. One should catch Gobius and throw them back into the river, they're already queuing up there. I catch them—and release them. No wind, no clouds. I want to drink, drink!

"To drink . . ."

"Hey, lad. You, I see, are unaccustomed to our sleeping-benches. Get off: they've brought concrete. Go on!"

Well, what a life. I left the crane, reeling. It was already light. Vehicle 00-77 had already dumped into the tub. I crawled, shovel in hand, and fell down in the concrete. I crawled again, hacked once, twice—and again fell down.

"Drive on! Fine!"

The crane brought the tub. For a long time we shouted for Nikolai; he had crawled into his usual hen-house and was sleeping so soundly that it was difficult to wake him up. The concrete was poured with a din, and there arose in the block such shouting, such a clamor, that my heart turned cold: someone had been buried.

"Nikolai! Nikolai! What happened?"

Nikolai was looking down and moving his lips.

"Nikolai! Answer me! Have the gals been buried?"

"Worse," he spat out. "What's with those wenches! The concrete mould has cracked. All the concrete is running to the devil. They've smashed it. Knock off!"

I climbed up like a cat and took a look: the opposite wall had cracked and come loose. The concrete gushed into the hole which had formed. The girls had saved themselves, were dragging the tampers, screaming, and clambering up along the steel reinforcement. One might expect the entire block to break up and fall into pieces like a matchbox. But the concrete oozed into the hole, murderously and quietly. All our labor had been in vain!

Dashkina's head was the first to appear, and immediately she spoke to Nikolai in indescribable fury:

"Oh, you red viper! Why did you dump it against the wall? Didn't see that it was weak, did you? Oh you . . ."

"Dasha, don't swear," said Tonia "He dumped properly."

She was flushed, dishevelled, as though she had emerged from hell, barely able to drag the tamper. I rushed to help her. She looked at me gratefully with her blue eyes and said:

"And you should have entrusted this to Tolia. He always dumps—on the button."

"You only want to sleep, to sleep!" Dashka hissed, preparing to slap Nikolai in the face.

He blinked his whitish eyelashes and was flushed, like a turkey.

"Go away!" he unexpectedly shouted shrilly. "I'll push you down!"

"You'll push me down?"

"Dashka, stop it, leave off, Dasha! Better go and call Moskalenko. Don't be irritated!"

For the first time I saw how people because of quarrels are ready to strike and beat one another, to hurt one another. Why: this was neither their kitchen-garden nor their home. For what reason? Why?

The works superintendent, carpenters, and foremen came running, shouted, argued, questioned Nikolai. The general conclusion was: the carpenters were at fault, those who put together the concrete mould.

All of us felt a little better now. But the mood was abominable. Dasha and Nikolai weren't speaking. Tonia sat on a beam in deep thought, pale, thin-faced, and so depressed, tired in her eyes and little figure, that I decided not to approach her.

A PLEASANT MORNING

But we didn't succeed in getting off so lightly. Dasha came running, alarmed, dismayed, and informed us that the bosses had gathered near the office, the construction site Party organization had arrived, and the entire brigade was being summoned there . . .

"This will be a hot day!"

Nikolai most of all started to yell and swagger.

"I, I'll t-tell them! I'll set them right! I'm not afraid, I've seen such people! The con-concrete mould-men caused the waste, but the concrete men are responsible? Do they think we're mute? They'll remember me. For a long time!"

"You go and tell them, Kolia!"

"I-I'll tell them! Afraid? No! I've been pouring concrete for ten years! They'll see!"

All the way he expatiated as though he had lost patience.

There were a lot of people at the office: 8.00 a.m., change of shift. Moskalenko stood on the porch, upset. What a night! I wouldn't want to be in Moskalenko's place now. The Party organizer came out on the porch.

It begins! . . .

"The regional committee has considered the results of the competition . . ."

What's this? We look at one another.

". . . The challenge banner of the regional committee of the CPSU has again been awarded to the Anna Moskalenko Brigade . . ."

A noise broke out in my ears. They were applauding.

"On their work depended the commencement of the damming of the Angara. The brigade has acquitted itself with honor . . ."

"They know nothing, shut up, Kolia!" whispered the girls.

". . . a disgraceful, scandalous attitude on the part of the sector leadership." The brigade has been standing for hours and only now did I learn that three quarters of the brigade had been sent to clean up rubbish and only one team has been pouring concrete—and that one "supplied" with a defective concrete mould!"

They brought out the red banner, again applause. Moskalenko, blushing like a girl, took it, began to utter the usual phrases in such instances, wandered off the subject, but then somehow came on to shortcomings and, having hit her stride, began to rail against the sector bosses, the electricians, the concrete-mould builders—so much so that she seemed to raise a cloud of dust.

The crowd laughed loudly, the Party organizer frowned, and made notations on a pad, but she, like a tiny bantam, poured out words, waving the banner:

"Ivan Mikitich, give us concrete, people are waiting!" He refers us to Gabaidullin: "Let him supply you." But Gabaidullin has gone to Kuz'mikha for potatoes. The deputy says: "It's not for me to do. Let the controller supply you." Why this mockery?! To what do we aspire? You are callous, uncaring people! The brigade stands idle! Well, bad luck to you, idlers!"

"Right, Moskalenchikha!" the crowd yelled. "Cut them up! Down with them!"

"I'll t-t-tell," Nikolai, full of resolve, crawled right through the railing on to the porch. He lay on his belly and rolled over, to general laughter. "I'll prove it! You think I'm afraid? No! I've been a concrete worker for ten years."

126

"Get to the point, to the point!"

"Isn't that the point? Yes? They think we're mute!. . ."

"Who are they, Kolia?"

"O.K. Hold your tongue, there!"

For a long time it was impossible to understand what Nikolai wanted to prove. It was obvious only that the man was boiling with resentment. Idleness, adding on, and a shortage of concrete.

Finally he blurted out:

"And if anyone makes a concrete mould like today, I'm going to belt him on the snout myself!"

"Well-l! Right on the snout. Never, Kolia!"

"You hold your tongue! Go on, make some defective work, and you'll see. For ten years I've done no defective work . . ."

Nikolai was dragged down from the porch with applause and laughter; he continued to wave his arms, and they tried to calm him down.

The sector chief then said that for today's waste the brigade of concrete mould builders was to be deprived of the progressive rate for work in excess of the plan and taken off the Board of Honor.

We had become the heroes of the day. The people thronged back to the block; Pet'ka the photographer came to the surface as if out of the ground and peremptorily ordered us to be photographed next to the banner. He clicked the shutter twenty times. True, no one to this day has received any photos, but on the other hand the fact was incontestable: our own sector photographer had snapped us.

Nikolai was flushed, perspiring, and very self-satisfied: he had succeeded amongst the crowd in telling his ideas to his neighbors.

"Let's go swimming!" he said. "I know a place. I've told no one about it, but I'll tell you: warm water, like tea!"

"Really?"

"I found it myself. Let's go, at home we'll have to wash anyway. And then you will help me move a chest of drawers."

I followed after him.

"Well, did I speak the truth?"

I flattered him. "Indeed you did, Nikolai."

HOW NIKOLAI'S WIFE HISSED AT HIM

In their room there was that delightful and fresh disorder which happens only on the joyous day of obtaining a new apartment. It was still clean and empty, but in the corner had been piled their beds and, leaning against the wall, the bed headboards; a curtain lays on the windowsill.

Nikolai's young, dark-browed, quiet wife began to fuss around the chest of drawers.

"Oh, why have you carried it by yourselves! You could have asked the drivers, you're exhausted."

"I should have asked those throat-cutters!" Nikolai muttered, wiping large beads of sweat from his forehead.

"Well, set it down there. Wash your hands quickly, we'll have breakfast. Have you been taking a drink somewhere again, my little red sunlight?"

"That's none of your business!" said Nikolai firmly.

His wife had remarkable eyes: dark-brown, moist, deep; when she raised her eyelashes and looked at me, it seemed she would now say something very important and good, and one wanted to reply accordingly.

"You're called Tolia? But I know you: Nikolai has told me much about you and praised and praised you. I'm simply called Ganna. Please excuse us, you see things are disorderly. I too have just come from work, and there isn't time for everything . . ."

"Do you work, Ganna?"

"I'm a motor mechanic. Sit down, do sit down! When guests feel shy, I myself am embarrassed."

"Well, I'm not hungry. I'll go on."

"Do I have to beat you?" Nikolai bellowed, grabbing me by the collar. "Sit down like a good lad as soon as you're invited!"

128

"Kolia! Kolia! Is this how you treat guests? You are out of your mind! Lord, when will I succeed in training you?"

Nikolai, not deigning to answer, flopped down in a chair.

"Serve what there is!"

"What interesting chairs you have!" I said bashfully.

"Kolia made them all himself. They're folding. And the bookcase. We don't live in one place for a long time, we move frequently, and that's why the furniture is like this."

"Why do you move?"

"Like all construction workers. A construction site finishes—we move on. What else can we do? We wander here and there. Our entire life is on the move . . ."

She said this sorrowfully and somewhat wearily, then smiled sadly and added:

"This construction site too will soon be finished. It's always like this for us: we live on and on in a barracks, but when they give us an apartment, it's on to another place. Someone else will live there."

"Why don't you stay?" I asked sympathetically.

"Well, are you joking! Who could keep Red from moving on?"

"Leave me alone!"

"Don't grumble, don't grumble! Well what are you ashamed of? Tell us?"

"I say this: you guzzle and stop sputtering . . ."

"Kolia is already looking for another place. Bad luck for me, but he received his leave in the spring. All the good people are on vacation, but he went off to the Bratsk Hydroelectric Station. 'Got to look around,' don't you see. What and how . . ."

"Nikolai! You were at the Bratsk Hydroelectric Station? And didn't say anything? How is it there?"

"How? Stones in the river—big ones! Breakers! Gates. Now they're building a city. And there's enough c-concrete! We'll make more defective things!"

129

"Tell about the midge," Ganna said.

"So what . . . it bites. We'll get used to it. One must get accustomed to that."

"Tolia, you eat, do. I know your life in the hostel. That's no home, there's no mama . . . Try some of our homemade soup."

"You . . . well, come . . . without ceremony," Nikolai muttered. "Gobble up what you want, you must. Ganka will always feed you. She's marvelous . . ."

"There . . . first time in a year he praised me," Ganna said with a smile but sadly. "Well, tell me, where have you come from, you miracle? Well? Red . . ."

"Go away!"

She, paying no heed to his awful grimaces, took hold of his ears and gently pulled. I bent down to my plate.

"Don't marry, Tol'ka," he said "Someone will then . . . pull your ears."

He blushed, puffed, narrowed his eyes, tried to scold threateningly—and couldn't.

VITAMIN "C"

There is no one. I lie on the bunk alone. I'm hot all over and feel sick. I just dreamed of apples. Cold, succulent, covered in dewdrops, sour-sweet. Excruciatingly tasty apples. This nightmare woke me up.

Today I finally understood why I feel ill and what I need. I want apples. One apple, half an apple, a little slice. I can't see the glass jars on the table with conserves, bits of herring.

I want apples!

In the morning I went to the market, but of course there were none there; for some reason I was exhausted and had no strength to travel into Irkutsk.

If I had 2000 rubles, I would get on an aircraft, fly to Moscow, and bring

130

back apples. Word of honor! I need nothing more. If I had 200 rubles, I would take a half month's leave at my own expense and make the trip . . .

I get my jacket with difficulty and turn the pockets inside out. Counting the small change and ill-fated three-ruble note, there are 32 rubles.

Oktiabrina, the cleaning woman, came in. Quietly, like a little mouse, she scrubs the floor, and when she crawls on all fours and wipes the boards with a wet cloth, I examine her lean hands, red from the water, narrow shoulders, and through an unfastened collar, thin dangling breasts. She's a mother, and neither she nor I are embarrassed. She has large dirty bare feet; she shuffles along the water-covered floor.

"Oktiabrina," I say. "Put a rug at the door and we'll wipe our feet."

She smiles gratefully, and only now do I begin to understand what pigs we all are.

"How old are you, Oktiabrina?"

"Twenty-two."

"Really? You look nineteen, not more."

"Oh, you're joking!" she laughs shyly and sadly. "I already have three children. I'm an old lady."

"No, you're very young." That's fine—I console her "It's good that you look younger. Only you're very weak. Isn't it difficult to scrub so many rooms? Don't clean them every day. We won't litter."

"Oh, never mind!"

"Have you been at the construction site for a long time?"

"Half a year. We were going to the Kurile Islands, but got stuck here."

"Where are you from?"

"We're from Kursk."

"Why did you leave?"

"We were bored there."

"And here?"

"Not bad . . ."

"Well, why didn't you go right on to the Kuriles?"

131

"We decided to live in Siberia for several years first, work, and then go on farther. It's interesting. One sees the world."

"Interesting?"

"Interesting."

"But don't you long for apples?"

"Yes."

She quietly disappears, and I with renewed strength plunge into nostalgia. How can I get apples? How?

Apples contain vitamins. Vitamin "C" it seems. Perhaps if I can get vitamin "C", I'll stop thinking about apples?

No one is present, and therefore I can swear and moan while dressing. It's entertaining, and I even begin to laugh. It's a long, long way to the drug store. I walk like a drunkard, acting without thinking properly. And all about me, sun, summer, heat! But nowhere—neither in the store, nor the canteen, nor the market—are there any apples, any pears, any cherries, or any strawberries. There's sauerkraut in jars. This is Siberia. When will these be brought in, or will they be brought?

On the little box of vitamins which I bought in the drug store is the date of issue: March 1952. How very old! They're little yellow balls, sweet on the outside and sour within. It's written that one should take 1-2 tablets a day. I swallow ten of them, and then more and more. An agonizing tremor from the sour taste runs through me, even leaves a light bad taste. That's the vitamin "C", which is what's in the apples! When you eat apples, there's also a sour taste in your mouth and your teeth are set on edge. And then there are grapes—cool, resilient, and the little yellow seeds are visible from the outside.

NATURAL APPLES

The little vitamin box stands on the window sill, but I'm already sick from them. I want apples!

Counting the pasted-up three-ruble note, I have 29 rubles. I get dressed

132

and think: doubtless I'll fall ill. My head buzzes; I can't grasp anything. If there were apples, like those I'd eaten at home, I'd be restored to health at once!

When I recover, I'll write a newspaper notice entitled "Bus-riding Olympiad": "The wrath, o goddess, of a passenger in the city of Irkutsk . . ." The Trojan War is nothing in comparison with what happens when boarding a bus. I stand and almost cry. I can't force my way into the bus. But I must if I am to go to Irkutsk for apples.

If the boss in charge of Irkutsk transport, the ancient Egyptian streetcars and patched up buses which go every hour, were in my presence, with what delight would I force him to ride in this bus day and night! And at the same time to addle the brains of those who don't bring in apples at the height of the summer, who don't give us a laundry, who delay our advance pay! A greater punishment wouldn't be required: the laundry would appear after the fifth trip.

All the same, after lunch I reached Irkutsk. The ticket had cost two rubles; I had 27 rubles left.

Stores. Hawkers' stands. Snack bars. Canteens, Restaurants. But no apples. I drank a glass of carbonated water, and within me a veritable fury arose. I became feverish and perspired. Does this mean I don't need the apples? Perhaps it's typhoid fever? No, no, I must continue to search!

It seemed to me that I would see apples somewhere in a shop window or some fruits. I'm just on the verge of seeing them. I ran, crawled, rushed up, eagerly ran my eyes over the counters—nothing, nothing!. . . Only jars and jars, and canned goods.

But in Moscow now on virtually every corner is a booth or stall with oranges, watermelons, grapes, and apples packed in straw, fragrant, crunchy. Am I losing my mind? It's already some sort of obsession. How far Moscow is!. . .

The last hope is the central market. I realized there weren't any there either, but I went.

My Lord, what isn't sold in this wide world! Fish—such as you never see in Moscow, meat of all varieties, cedar nuts, pickled cucumbers, casks of honey, sauerkraut, and flour! A happy noise, hubbub, crush, beckoning!

"Tolia! Tol'ka! Tol'ka-a!"

Is someone calling me? I turned round . . . and almost gasped. In the fish row, behind the scales, in a tarpaulin apron with an enormous fish in his wet hands . . . stood Grishka the greedy, my former fellow traveler.

"Grishka! Hello. How did you come to be here?"

"Oho-ho! Business! A whole movie! See what I'm doing. They spoke the truth, that you won't perish in Siberia."

"Grishka, tell me quickly, weren't you going to the Bratsk Hydroelectric Station?"

"To hell with it! We arrived, understand, in a forest, locked up in the wild—neither house nor home, and we were to cut timber! We scouted around, met the locals. "Why," they said, "we live like wolves, no money, and whatever we earn we gobble up ourselves. We haven't seen potatoes for half a year." They work in dens, the gnats bite, our mugs are swollen—look! Well, I was on my way—back, to the Irkutsk Hydroelectric Station. Also awful! I went to Baikal. They told me the fishermen at Ol'khon are making a mint. I fished for a while, but saw that wasn't for me. Question of luck: some made thousands, others lost their shirt. Now I've found something: I bring in omul* from the Ol'khon. There, on the shore, the fishermen sell a whole fish for a ruble, but here it's twelve for a kilo . . . I've already taken over 2,000 rubles. The transport is difficult, you may get caught. Want an omul? I'll give it to you for half price! A fat rascal, look!"

He lifted the large fish by its tail, but I felt ill merely from looking at it.

"How are Dimka Strepetov, Vasek, Ivan Bugai?"

"Those good-for-nothings, they're working. They don't mind! Worthless people. They laugh and say: "It's fine here." They almost killed Leshka."

"How was that?"

---

* (sea fish of salmon family, also found in Lake Baikal—transl.)

"Playing cards! I realized from the outset what a bird he was. He sat down to play with a group of fellows, won 1500 from his pals, and cleared out. Where do you run in the forest? They caught him, and he said: I was playing a joke. Oh, they rebuked him, he cried, stopped playing cards . . . So, tell me, what are you up to? Settled in Irkutsk?"

"I'm a concrete worker here on a construction site . . ."

"Well, I knew it! Idiot! As soon as I arrived I sniffed around and thought: no, this kvass is not for us. If you want to quit that dirty work I'll take you in to my business. Without associates it's difficult for me. We'll haul as a pair: it's safer. We'll make about 8,000 each and take off for home. We'll even take some to Moscow; there they make 20 rubles a kilo. A splendid fish! Super!"

I weakly waved my hand and quickly, staggering, went on, paying no attention to Grishka's surprised exclamation: "What's with you? What's with you? Where are you going?"

Gasping, I circled the bazaar, then stopped to think: where was I running?

And at that instant, right in front of me, I saw the apples.

True, my head was buzzing so that I could have mistaken any little green turnips for apples. No. Beneath the scale in a little box lay tiny green pimples, rather like greens, which the wind blows into the garden each spring. A tall, likeable man of Caucasian appearance stood at the scales in an apron and shouted gaily:

"Here, real Caucasian natural apples: 'Belyi nalivs.' "*

They cost 30 rubles a kilogram. I bought half a kilo, put one in my mouth, crunched it with my teeth—and felt a sharp extremely sour taste, the real taste of apples. Do you know what that's like?

Later I came to my senses sitting below some small chest on boards. Strange that a policeman hadn't taken me along.

* (a particular kind of apple—transl.)

135

I went to the bus stop and repeated the "busriding olympiad." About four hours later, or more, I reached home. My last strength was spent climbing the steps to the hostel.

Well, a speculator had demonstrated he could supply greens to Siberia from the Caucasus more easily than some graduates of the trade technical schools—hm!—could from the Ukraine or Central Asia. How ridiculous!

These were my last coherent thoughts that day. In the night an ambulance took me to the hospital.

End of the Third Notebook

A PAGE OF MY PAD. ROUGH COPY

"Mama, my dear, hello!

How are you? Why don't you write? How are your eyes? I received only your first letter in which you were sighing and worrying so much about me.

Don't! For heaven's sake, don't worry about anything! If you only knew how nice it is here, how fine I am, how successful everything has turned out! The lads in the hostel are excellent, our brigade is remarkable, the most outstanding at the construction site.

In Siberia, it turns out, there is a lot of milk. I'm already tired of it: milk, milk at every step.

Our work is fine, very interesting. I have no regrets coming here. As regards my belongings, don't worry, I assure you again: I have a suit, it's a long time until winter, and I'll set something aside from my first pay for a coat.

We're happy here: there are clubs, a cinema, dances. And if you want to, you can sit on a bus and go in to Irkutsk—there is everything your heart desires. In the market you can get anything: eggs, omul, fruits.

Who told you about midges and mosquitoes? I haven't seen a single midge or mosquito as long as I've lived here. They're in the god-forsaken taiga, but our nature and weather are exactly like the greater Moscow area, absolutely no difference, only here there is a sea of flowers and high, impenetrable hills . . .

I have a request: if you should see Sasha incidentally, give him my greetings and tell him that I wanted to write but don't know the address of their new apartment.

That's all for now.

Take care of yourself. Don't worry about me. Don't you dare borrow any money and send it to me! Do you know how much concrete workers earn here? Up to 1500 rubles per month! What am I to do with so much money? I've decided to save a bit and then send it to you. Your fur coat is completely worn out!

Farewell. I kiss you tenderly.

P.S. Oh, yes! For several days I was a bit sick here. You asked that I tell you the truth about my health, so I do so. But it's a trifle, don't worry, it's the change in climate.

Please tell Viktor not to write letters to me. I don't reply to him, but he writes and writes."

THE FOURTH NOTEBOOK

WARD No. 5

"Oh, you good-for-nothing! You nonentity. I'm not going to talk with you anymore. Move your bed out. Go to the ward for the insane; there they'll straighten your brain out! You get out, or I will!"

"Mishka, you're infuriated . . ."

"Yes, infuriated, because a normal person can't stick it out with you here. Don't you understand: some whimperers came here, like lords, three inches taller than a jug and their mother's milk not dried on their lips—and presume to open their yap. They, don't you see, don't like it here! Oh, if I could only thrash you, I'd wear out twenty belts on you!"

"Because you haven't seen anything better!"

"I've seen, brother. I lived in your Moscow for six years, know the entire Stromynka inside and out, every day at 8:45 a.m. ran along Okhotnaia to school. I know Moscow better than you, milksop, and know Siberia even better! You want everything to be ready. You want to travel from Irkutsk to Iakutia by subway, and a Bolshoi Theatre to open at Kuz'mikha. But there are jungles, do you know? Jungles! Alaska! The Antarctic! A man who goes 100

139

versts away from the railway is a Cook, a Magellan, a Przheval'skii! Siberia no one has touched, no one knows it, nor understands it. Siberia is an undiscovered planet, enough wealth to satisfy the entire world! Do you know that we are now sitting on top of coal? Yes, yes, there's coal under your bed! At Kuz'mikha they fuel their stoves with it, they walk to the foot of the mountain and dig it out of a pit with a shovel; go and see for yourself. You came—did you know where you were going? You were invited to discover, to get in up to your knees, up to your neck in a swamp to lay a road, and you screech: Siberia turned out to be bad, there's no subway. Get out, or I'll kill you!"

"But can't we open up and be like human beings!"

"What does "like human beings" mean? Perhaps you'd like to receive a cottage? To ride to work in a ZIM? But who's going to make the ZIMS?! Four unhappy decades ago a rotten, ragged, barbaric Russia began to breathe fresh air, began to build something. Hungry mouths, naked bellies, darkness, one and a half Fords in the entire Empire, and they were foreign—they grasped fire with bare hands, chopped firewood, went without food, performed miracles, saved the world from fascism—and built, marched onward, went on. But you already want to ride in a ZIM? You decided that everything is finished? Everything, my dear friend, is only beginning! Yes! Only beginning! You come and expect everything to be all ready, expect an apartment with a telephone and gas, expect Siskin not to drink anymore, and the markets to be piled high with pineapples. Perhaps I too want a pineapple, those which on the Arbat, in the fruit store, are 16 rubles a kilo! But, my dear, first Moscow must be built here! The country consists, unfortunately, not only of capitals. In Irkutsk, the largest city of Eastern Siberia, there is only one streetcar line, and people still haven't seen a trolleybus. Understand? Around the virgin land are wilds! It's premature to speak of the quiet life, premature . . . Whosoever wants in our time to live honorably and like a human being, and not like a parasite—he develops the virgin land with his own hands, and doesn't bitch!"

"All this, Misha, I do understand. Remember how we agreed that if

America had undergone even half of what Russia underwent, it would not have achieved even a hundredth part . . ."

"Look at the spirit, look at the rhythm. Why go so far? Look at what we suffered just in one war! They have only become rich, only raked it in. But we gave our lives, our sweat and blood. Your father perished, but for what did he die? What will we perish for, if it will prove to be necessary?"

"Misha, all this I understand . . . You don't need to prove to me that our country accomplished miracles in an unprecedented period of time. That Siberia is an undiscovered planet is a bit new to me, but it doesn't bother me; I agree to discover it . . ."

"He 'agrees'! No one's asking you, no one's bowing down before you! You must do it. You understand, no one's asking you; if you don't want to, go to all the devils and live your life quietly, comfortably, cosily, and dirty your hands. Plug away! How many people are plugging away! But only if you're a real man, you won't be able to live quietly. You have to make great discoveries! Listen! A m-a-n!"

"I agree. I must. I must! That's why I came here. But when I encounter a swinish attitude, when I see how many parasites there are in the world . . ."

"Then you lose heart, and you cry "mama"?"

"No. But I do suffer."

"Become a parasite yourself. I'm suggesting a good way out for you. Brilliant! Well?"

" . . ."

"Why are you silent?"

"Get lost!"

"He starts scolding. Not so bad. Let's sit down together and start wailing. Perhaps there'll be fewer parasites. But you!!! But you, what will you do so that they become fewer. Are you only going to cry? Are you frightened? Haven't you tried to smack them on the snout? Your first steps at the construction site you commemorated by learning how to add on? Fine! You'll go far . . . No-o, brother. You can't live on the fence, nor stand your ground by saying it's no concern of yours. For forty years there have existed only two

141

poles—if you're not with us, you're against us. What is the weariness of struggle, this panic in the face of a mess? I'm staggered! You are reasoning that everyone builds up merely his own well-being, that parasites live in the world better than honorable people! You're whining, whimpering, snivelling, frightened! Of what?! Use your hands, get callouses, but don't snivel, don't hang about underfoot! Do what you must, but don't jabber! Oh, I h-a-t-e it . . . !''

"You're straight, like a board, you'd merely write reports! Ultimately, every person has the right to search and endure!''

"No! You have no such right! Cover your head with a blanket, shut up and endure, but don't bitch. I'm fed up, you understand, fed up!''

He grasped my hand and left quickly. I stayed seated, furious and irritated, and again all my thoughts were mixed up and confused. The wind banged the small ventilation window, pulled at the billowing cheesecloth which covered the window. Suddenly there was noise, and steps in the corridor. The voice of the nurse:

"Chief doctor! Chief doctor! Ol'khonskii of Ward 5 is lying on the steps, attendants!''

I leapt up and rushed downstairs. Near the exit to the courtyard, on the concrete porch, the attendants were lifting Misha. The steps were covered with blood. His face had gone yellow, like a corpse, and he was unconscious. The bandage had torn off, and blood directly from the wound had spattered on the stone steps. When he was carried to the dressing station, traces extended along the stairways and corridors. The doctors rushed about, injected camphor, and called out: "Oxygen, oxygen!''

I began to shiver. They carried Misha and put him to bed, as yellow as before and unconscious. In the corridor they scrubbed the floor.

THERE'S NO PEACE UNDER THE OLIVE TREES

There's no tranquility on earth, even in a hospital. People break into my life and disturb me, they call and demand; my head is breaking apart from new

142

thoughts, new feelings. People, diverse and dissimilar, crowd my soul and don't let me sleep at night.

The hospital is overcrowded. The construction site suddenly showed a completely different aspect to me: I saw how many accidents occur, how many people are ill. The ambulance almost never stands idle: it brings in the sick and maimed constantly. There were no places in the Gastric Ward, so they put me in the surgical section.

In the fifth sector was a concrete worker, a reception clerk like me: he had lingered at the tub, the driver backed up his vehicle, pressed him against the tub, and broke two ribs. This could have happened to me.

A dump truck fell from the viaduct and was smashed to smithereens. The driver succeeded in jumping clear, but the foreman went down in the cab. They brought him in still alive, but he died on the operating table.

At night they brought in a girl with a knife wound in the back. Their heels clicked in the corridor, they banged against the bed. And they placed her right in the passageway, near our door: there were no places. Her fiance had stabbed her: he came to her drunk, began to pester, to accuse her of something, then drew out a knife and stabbed her. In the morning he rushed in, pale, frightened to death, and brought her a bottle of milk; they sat together, held hands, and sobbed . . .

I wonder at doctors, policemen, and judges. They see life only through sufferings: accidents, misfortunes, crimes. One would suppose them to be the most dismal and weary people. But our doctors, for example—happy, carefree, flourishing. Without exception they are women. Polina Frantsevna, the doctor who makes the round in our ward, doesn't show off, doesn't pretend cheerfulness; she simply seems to regard us as idlers and spineless creatures:

"Well, well, now are you still crying "mama"! My Lord, how awful—syringe. Well, are you going to cry or get well? Well, get up and swat a fly. They're breeding a menagerie here, lie about like pigs, the closets are a mess! They're used to their wives working for them! I'll break you of that habit! Get up, lazybones, pick up the towel!"

"I can't with the right . . ."

143

"Try with the left! You know how to play dominos, you see how they bang against one another, so don't smash the table. You're all malingerers! You're all one of a piece—into the river with you."

"Polen'ka, my dear, wait just a moment; we're beginning to rot under your treatment."

"Sure, with a mug such as yours, rot away! Look, let the chin grow, like a merchant. Well, don't try to get away with something. The towel!"

But we know the nurses must drive out the flies, and the flies cruise about in the dozens, but we pursue them for a whole hour, clamber up on chairs, move forward on a wide front and swat them until not a single one is left.

Splendid gymnastics!

Only today for the first time did I see Polina Frantsevna concerned, almost frightened—when they brought in Misha. She was pale, didn't make jokes, came in every five minutes and took his pulse.

Later she brought in a tall structure with a long glass cylinder filled up to the top with blood—like syrup in the stalls with carbonated water. Misha already had regained consciousness. Polina Frantsevna rubbed his arm with alcohol near the elbow, inserted the needle with a crunch—it made my flesh creep—and blood began slowly to flow into Misha's body.

We silently watched this solemn action. The blood went drop by drop.

"Is it all right?"

"O.K."

Silence. We sit, holding our breath.

"Misha, it doesn't hurt you?"

"No, I don't feel it. Do I have to lie for long like this?"

"Lie quietly. As much as possible."

And Polina Frantsevna left.

Misha, smiling, watched the level in the cylinder go down—the glass walls were left yellow, with spots.

"Hm! . . . How strange! someone else's blood. Someone, somewhere, donated it, and now it will be inside me. If one could only get to know the

144

person! But suppose it was a pretty girl? And now you have a "blood relationship" with her! Splendid, huh? See here, Tolia, people even give blood to one another. You see?"

A week ago Misha went home after work. On a wasteland, beyond a swamp, he heard a cry:

"Help! Oh, help me! Don't pass by, where are you going?"

Some worker was in front of Misha, heard, and quickened his pace, almost ran. Misha shouted after him: "Coward!"—and hurried toward the voice. Three drunks had surrounded a woman. Either they had assaulted her or wanted to rape her. Misha fell upon them and sent them flying. The woman grabbed her basket and fled crying, but the drunks started a fight. Misha fought so fiercely that they, cursing, retreated and disappeared into the darkness. Then he noticed blood gushing from his right hand: they had stabbed him with a knife.

He went to the hospital.

Misha is a Buriat. He was born at Baikal, on Ol'khon Island, and his surname was Ol'khonskii. When I awakened in the morning and saw him for the first time, I expected him to speak some broken language, rather like Chinese. He smiled and asked absolutely without any accent:

"Well, you're alive? Yet another victim of civilization."

I still can't get used to the fact that a person with such slanted eyes, Mongol cheekbones, bronze-colored and stocky, speaks such pure Russian, with a Moscow-accent, that he beats me in all arguments, and quotes Campanella and Rousseau—books that I have never seen. We argue day and night. Because of these arguments and various occurrences, I don't notice that I'm slowly recuperating.

MY OWN PEOPLE

Through the window of our ward the Angara and the pontoon bridge across it are clearly visible. We stand there for a long time and look and look.

145

The hospital is on the edge of the city, no one comes along, there are no vehicles, only the ambulance, again on call, again grief somewhere . . . It's quiet, deserted. From afar there is a rumbling, but we are on an island.

"I can't stand it," Misha said. "They're just on the verge of opening the spillways. I'll go crazy here. Sitting here like a prisoner in an idiotic dressing gown! These dressing gowns are a cunning idea, they remind you every minute: you're not a person, you're ill, ill!"

Misha is an engineer and the secretary of the Komsomol organization of his section. During the reflooding he was to be on the bridge itself. He bites his lips and growls. His engineer friends come to see him, and we are brought up to date about events on the principal installations. Several days, still several days more!

"Polina, discharge me! I swear that I'll be careful."

"Stay put, you hero," the doctor waves her hand. "I'm not going to release you earlier than two weeks from now, so don't even think about it! If you behave yourself—perhaps a week and a half . . ."

"Polen'ka, Polinochka, dear, golden, little Polly, I'll die here!"

"Just try."

"I'll hang myself!"

"I'll cut you down and revive you."

"You're monsters! Butchers!"

"Swear, go on, swear."

"M-m-m . . ."

I myself am trembling, awaiting the analyses; tomorrow the x-rays. If everything is positive, I'll be discharged, and Misha looks at me beforehand with hatred. Polina Frantsevna brought him a whole pile of books at his request: there are Wells, Jack London, and Conan Doyle, and three volumes of *Jean Christoph*. Misha leafs through thoughtfully, turns the pages, but his thoughts are far away . . .

"What was that tooting? A locomotive? Where?"

Again to the window. An ancient little locomotive pulls a platform with rails and has covered half the sky with smoke. They are cleaning up the last segments of the East Siberian main line from the construction site to Baikal, and there, where the Moscow-Vladivostok express sometimes flew by me, now remained only a pile of railway ties . . . The trains passed through mountains on the new route. The Angara is deserted up to Baikal itself: not a light nor a sound. She awaits the sea. Baikal itself, thanks to the Irkutsk dam, will rise a meter and become wider.

. . . Somehow I lay alone in the ward and was miserable, looking at the ceiling. A strange feeling: powerlessness and loneliness.

The door opened, and a woman in a white dressing gown entered. I expected no one and didn't turn my head. She approached me. It was Moskalenko. Tiny, entangled in the gown, she sat down cautiously.

"Leonid came running, said they've taken Anatolii to the hospital. What's the matter with you?"

"Well . . . I don't know myself. It's so annoying . . ."

"Never mind, Tolia, you'll get well. We have excellent doctors. Valia is taking your place now at the reception point, but it's not for her. Without you it's become boring."

"You needn't say . . ."

"I'm telling the truth. Only you need to be more courageous. Our people are rather—audacious, if you indulge them all, they'll ride roughshod over you . . . Here's a present for you. Where can I put it? On the night table?"

"You shouldn't have!"

"It's O.K., eat it and regain your strength. Don't pine. You know, there is everything to look forward to in life. Oh! It's long, Anatolii, and not easy, much strength is required. The girls will come to visit you. Perhaps you need money? How's the food here?"

"No, fine, it's all right."

"Another tenner won't hurt. There, I'm putting it on the night table. Give it to the nurse, she'll run out and buy some eggs or something for you."

"Oh, you needn't. I don't require anything!"

"Keep lying down, get well. Believe me, everything will be fine. Believe me!"

147

She smiled a tender, kind smile, and her face, almost an old woman's, sparkled with little wrinkles. Again in her eyes there was something melancholy and reticent. She left quietly, and I lay back and thought: who is she really? In the morning of the next day I crept out of the ward into the courtyard. Grass, benches, sunshine; some patients had formed a circle and were playing a game of Preference, others were playing dominos.

"They're calling for you," said a nurse passing by.

I glanced around distrustfully. Again a woman had come to visit me. It was Tonia.

She had dressed up in her violet dress, her braids tautly pressed against her head; she was fresh, glowing, slender, and embarrassed.

We approached each other and didn't know what to talk about. She proffered a small parcel with gifts, and I was ready to vanish into thin air. I had on a darned, mouse-grey dressing gown and underneath, long underwear with ties and slippers on my bare feet. How wild and helpless I must appear next to her! The patients turned around to look at us, the group of Preference-players stopped their game and stared. To hell with them!

"Let's sit down?"

"Hm . . ."

"Tonia, thank you . . ."

Some nurses came by, and we fell silent until they passed.

"Are you better?"

"As you see . . . I'm already strolling about."

"Fine . . . Tamara and Olia send you greetings."

"Thank you . . ."

"Do you want books? The *Scarlet Sails* is there. Sweet cherries have appeared in the market . . ."

"Well, why all this? When I was healthy—nothing was given to me, even a book, but when I'm ill, everything at once. It means I should fall ill more often."

"Don't gripe."

"Tonia . . ."

148

"What?"

"But . . . have you finished the shore wall?"

"H-hm. The reflooding is to be in a few days. Things are moving on!
. . . Great rush."

. . . And, after lunch, an entire platoon marched in: Pet'ka, the photographer, Kubyshkin with Galia, Leonid . . . and our old acquaintance from the canteen—the "criminal investigator" Sania. Lenia was right: he had succeeded in recruiting him, true, not in his own brigade—in a subsidiary one, but he had clothed and fed him, and the "criminal investigator" had become a dandy!

Zakhar Zakharych passed on five packs of "Kazbek" cigarettes and a chocolate bar. Never in my life had I so many nice things at once. The entire ward gobbles up my candies and cookies.

The "platoon" of guests pestered me, patted me on the shoulder, laughed such that even I saw how they were trying to reassure me.

I don't belive this is real. Somehow I feel awkward and ill-at-ease. In the hospital I saw not merely people's misfortunes and sufferings, I found out something else that I hadn't understood before.

Evening. An extraordinary event just occurred. The entire hospital is in an uproar. They're beseiging the doctors. Polina Frantsevna has locked herself in the office and doesn't open the door, and the patients stand in front, shout, scratch, implore. The reflooding is to be the day after tomorrow. It has been announced officially. Mishka Ol'khonskii reminded everyone of this. He had obtained a suit and boots, thrown off his dressing gown, changed, climbed over the fence, and escaped.

ON LOVE, BUGS, AND SOME OTHER THINGS

Alarm! Alarm! Something had happened at home, but what I couldn't understand. The room was different, the air was different, the world likewise.

Had Kubyshkin married? Had he removed his bed? Yes, he and Galia had obtained a room in the first settlement and embarked upon a very difficult and complicated family life. We were orphaned. But this was not the main thing. There was something else.

Zakhar Zakharych was about, had shaved, smelled of eau de cologne. During the reflooding period the drivers are to be transferred to tents on the Angara shore. They sleep there, and have a canteen and medical center.

Zakhar Zakharych, in a fresh shirt, smart, squeaking boots, seemed ten years younger. He paced from mirror to wardrobe and sang—I heard for the first time how he sings—in a funny, droning, broken bass:

> Our locomotive, speed ahead,
> There's a stop in the commune.
> Another route we do not have . . .

"Well, old chap, you're an imposing fellow!" Pet'ka said, observing how the old man ties his necktie. "Where are you going like this! It would be a different matter if it were for a party!"

"You're a little fool, Petro," replied Zakhar Zakharych good-naturedly. "Where were you brought up?"

"Why?"

"Why, why! You've mussed up the bed, thrown your dirty socks about—and you sit down, satisfied. Well, why are you grinning? It's the worst sort of man who can't look after himself."

"It's O.K. with me."

"Do you know what? I can see what you're worth from how you shave."

"What am I worth now?"

"One kopeck, of course."

"Ho-ho-ho! No, old man, honest-to-God, you should get married. Word of honor, the time has come. Take a simple peasant woman, a young one—every day she'll sew starched collars. Like a bayonet!"

"Collars I can do myself . . ."

"Well then in general, for respectability! Right, old man, do get married.

Your turn has come. Just look at yourself, what a fiancé has gone to waste! Huh?"

"In this respect, Petro, I'm a hundred times better than you . . ."

"So why the conversation? Kubyshkin in the vanguard, and you next. Tol'ka and I will try somehow."

"Hm . . . No, Petro."

"Why not, why not! Do you think I don't know where you bring your money? I saw, I saw who does your laundry. The wench isn't bad, single, she has only four kids—and it will keep you occupied in your old age."

"Stop it, Petro."

"Aha, I've caught you!"

"At what?"

"Never mind, old man, don't be embarrassed. I'll be your matchmaker, O.K.? And after you, we'll arrange my marriage."

"Don't blabber nonsense, you young buck. With ideas like that, it's still too early for you to get married. You still need a thrashing."

"That's also true . . . I'd better wait a bit. Oh, I'll play about as I please and get married in my old age!"

"That's your business. They say truly: God didn't give intelligence, look at the cripple."

"Old man, you know they're all talking nonsense? You know they're talking nonsense that one must live all his life with one woman? To change them is wrong, to run after them is wrong! Isn't it boring, old man?"

"I don't know. You see, it's different for everyone. You know that people are very different. I say to you, Petro, in my view it's like this: either you love or you don't. Perhaps one loves once, but such, lad, that it lights up your entire life . . . You still play about: you flirt with one—make a vow; flirt with another—vow again. Thus, your love isn't real . . . Others use themselves up for trifles, and then shout: there's no love, a family is prejudice, if one wants it—one loves; if it distresses you, cast it aside! But such persons, Petro, never learned what love really is in this world!"

"And what is it?"

151

"What can I tell you? Grow up—you'll find out. Love is real only for a real man. Remember that. You've gotten me excited. Where did I lay my wallet?"

I listened to their conversation in silence. Pet'ka, although he chattered, obviously also had been moved.

"Old man! What would you do if you were young again?"

"Young, Petro?"

"M-h-m!"

"But who knows? Probably the same things I did."

"A tank-driver too?"

"Well, yes."

"No, I don't mean that. Not that! If you were in my place, in Tol'ka's place. If you were to become young suddenly. You're old, you've lived life, you've seen everything. Tell us what you have learned. So we don't have to search anew. For example, why to live, how to live? When you pass away, you'll take everything with you. You old people are silent, stingy. Give it to us . . ."

"What is there to be greedy about? Were I young, Petro, I would look after my heart. I wasn't sorry once, and now it hurts. Surely you, young men, will remember?"

"Old man! We'll take care of our heart. Tell us more. Take nothing with you!"

"You are funny . . . I have nothing to take with me, Petro."

"I mean, concepts of life. Well, what would you do now in my place."

"Now?"

"Now!"

"I would build the Irkutsk Hydroelectric Station."

"Really?"

"The truth."

"So are we right? Are we on the right track?"

"You are . . . Pass the iron . . . I can't leave like this, I'll press them once more . . . If you start such a conversation, Pet'ka, you should know one thing: one must live life to the full. So that everything in it will be great: if love, then true love, and not pretense; if friendship, then real friendship; if joy, then genuine joy, and not a bagatelle; if sorrow, then let it be sorrow as great as an ocean. Happy people live thus, who don't seek trifles, nor live only for themselves. Such as godparents. In living your long life you should have a purpose, do things with your hands, that people may thank you . . . I don't even mention, Petro, those scoundrels who live at the expense of others, They should be suppressed, like bugs. As soon as there's light, they disappear into the cracks—they can't be seen and want to conceal themselves from others. What a joy to live like a bug! One needn't understand anything of life, one may spit on your own and other's feelings, and creep about in such filth until your death."

"Br-r! How you do express yourself, old man."

"I would say more. Look again—it's offensive! Oh, how much stupidity there is in a man! Is there happiness in money, or happiness in a full and well-dressed belly, or in a six-room apartment? These are trifles, small change, which goes without saying! Happiness—is within one; happiness—is a storm, a battle; it's—the sun in your heart, of which there's enough for others and yourself and which, after your death, remains to wander about the world, to excite, to call, to illuminate! Oh, Petro, why do you ask me about life? This is something you must feel, you must have a human head and heart, and not a bug's. You must love life, Petro, and not be a swine. So! You have excited me, but you most likely are laughing . . . O.K., let's put a stop to clarity. I've doubtless already forgotten something. Well, I'll remember and pick it up again. All the best."

"We'll drop by, old man! Don't catch cold there. It's chilly at night. Won't you take my blanket along, hm? Old man!"

"Never mind! Your 'old man' is an old soldier. He's used to sleeping at night in the snow, covered by a little rain, a little wind under his head, and the imps even shook it up. You're invited!"

Zakhar Zakharych slammed the door, clattered along the corridor, and far into the darkness, beyond the windows, his heavy steps and his jarring, droning bass were heard:

> We have no other way,
> Rifle in our hands . . .

The old man sang on! And then Len'ka burst into the room with a crash. Dirty, filthy, out of breath.

"Scarecrows! Why are you sitting about?! They're opening the spill-way!"

IT BEGINS

The dawn was damp and cold. Milky patches of fog hung above the Angara. For some reason there was the smell of snow—perhaps the wind brought this air from faraway mountains. My teeth were chattering—from the coolness and the excitement. A thin floodgate, on one side of which are the waters of the Angara and, on the other, our foundation ditch. Two self-propelled excavators facing one another stretched out their booms from the shores.

In the quiet they began to blow up the earth; their motors howled terri-bly. With a clang that shook the ground underfoot, their large-toothed buck-ets stretched into the levelled earth. The "Jupiters" began to creak: the cam-eraman began to shoot.

A sigh came from the crowd: water had appeared. One more bucket and a foamy, dirty little stream struck out below with clods of earth into the ditch. The excavator operators began to hurry up, as though something depended on speed: the booms almost whistled in the air. Already a tor-rent, noisy, muddy, flows downward, washes away the spillway—and . . . the water bursts out!

It was majestic and terrible. Crashing down into the ditch with a roar and

154

a rumble, the water envelops the spillway, the excavators started to back up on their tracks, moved back, away from the waterfall. On the shore people were shouting and throwing stones into the water. Those roads on which we had run and hurried, on which the drivers had travelled and broken their springs, disappeared forever under the water; the rocks on which we assembled before a shift had vanished under the water; the little square where the canteen stood and the elephants—the 25-ton MAZ trucks—had gathered were gone . . . The office on whose porch they had presented the banner to us and where Nikolai made his speech . . . No one would ever again see these memorable places so dear to us. Perhaps a diver will go down to inspect the foundation after a hundred years or so.

My Pet'ka was growling, moaning, and clicking his camera. Someone yelled happily:

"Brothers, I've left my shovel there! . . ."

But "there" everything was turbulent, the water was muddy, dirty, chips, rubbish, beams, and boards spun in whirlpools. The piers and waste gates disappeared under the water.

A second stage began: they opened another spillway. Water filled the ditch from both ends.

Already it was like a full cup. We stand on the viaduct—it no longer seems high, for the muddy water seethes under our very feet and whirls with patches of brown foam. It seemed that now the Angara itself is passing through the station, through the opened passages, and will not make a bend.

But the river is by no means intended to go here. Having filled the abyss of the ditch, it flowed along its former bed, and in the ditch the water became calm and stopped running.

The main thing was still ahead: to force it to turn! They will dump rocks and blocks from the bridge because the river still was not partitioned off. A day remained of my sick leave, but I went out with the shift. How could one wait when at the shore yard our brigade was making concrete blocks?!

THE BATTLE

At first it looked like a holiday. The pontoon bridge was decorated with flags and posters. It was a lovely warm summer evening. From the settlements hurried crowds of dressed-up girls, old men, entire families with small children, as though going to an outdoor party. An anxious tension already could be felt on the approaches to the shore. Hundreds of trucks were parked in even rows. Mountains of concrete blocks, entire piles of rocks; the steam Shkodas were angrily growling and puffing.

The drivers start and race the motors, assemble in groups around the radiators, laugh, clap their mittens; the loudspeaker announces: "Comrade Popov, come to the headquarters . . ." Noise, talking, laughter. At the bridge itself the cameramen have built a tower and are fiddling with their cameras. No one is allowed on the bridge, it's deserted and trembles under the immense pressure of the water. It is surprisingly short, seemingly you could reach the other shore with your hand: they had dammed the Angara to the limit, and the water, like bottle-glass in color and bending resiliently, shoots out from under the pontoons, smooth, compact, and having flown only seven meters, disperses into white breakers, hisses, and splashes. Never in the world had a river with such a strong current been reflooded.

At 7:00 p.m. everything began, very quietly and cautiously. The excavator clanked and poured the first buckets of rocks into the dumpers, the dump truck started with a jerk and went on to the bridge. The trucks started to emit smoke, were enveloped in exhaust fumes, and lined up for the excavator. The loaded trucks, howling and honking, sped on to the bridge, backed up, and dumped the rocks.

The crowd on the shore was worried, some shouted:

"Carry it there! Where are you going! Don't fall off!"

"They'll catch it a mile away!"

Some blocks skipped for several moments on the surface; the crushed stone was carried away like dust. The Angara was showing its teeth!

The words of the head of the construction site were broadcast: the drivers are to work uninterruptedly until tomorrow evening. Twenty-four hours! If not more . . . No one knows how the Angara will behave.

But the "MAZs" roared, went on and on, dumped and dumped. Smoke from the exhaust pipes stretched like blue ribbons from shore to shore, the flags quivered in the smoke. The crashing of rock, the waterfall noise of the river, snatches of sentences from the loudspeakers: "Be careful! Don't break the rhythm! Everything depends on you . . ."

"Zakharych! Zakharych!"

The old man was hauling rocks. He leaned out of the small window, waved at Pet'ka and me, and disappeared behind the smoke and dust.

We ran to "overtake" him at the excavator. Pet'ka clicked his camera five times: the old man smiled with embarrassment and gave threatening looks: get out, don't bother me!

"Zakharych! Let us into the cab!"

"Can't. We are ordered not to take anyone. It's dangerous, lads!"

At the bridge there was chaos. The duty personnel were exhausted, pleading, imploring, scolding:

"Get off the road! Leave the bridge!"

The dump trucks penetrated into the crowd like tanks, quickly, without a second's rest. The rocks were dumped and dumped into the river, but it carried and carried them away . . . Yellow bubbles and whirlpools for a moment—and again smooth, lively, crystal-clear water, such that your head spins when you look into it.

I had read somewhere about the Angara and come across the word: aquamarine water. I don't know what this color is, but undoubtedly it is precise. There is no simple word to convey the staggering beauty of this implausible, unnatural water. It's transparent, like crystal; it plays elusively, like a precious stone; it's aq-ua-ma-rine! This evening the cameramen spoiled hundreds of meters of film while endeavoring to photograph the colors. From time to

157

time they grabbed their cameras and intently filmed the breakers and the torrent. Pet'ka conceded that he too had lost half a film-roll on the water; he knew that it wouldn't succeed, that these marvelous plays of color couldn't be caught by anything, but still couldn't resist trying. This can only be seen, and I look, everyone looks, greedily, excitedly.

The hundreds of vehicles rock the bridge. It bends, rises, comes down, and creaks. Some pontoons submerge, others jump up, and the trucks sway on them. Smoke! Smoke! Darkness came unexpectedly. Hundreds of spotlights lit up. It resembles a filming at night. Noise, voices,—a fair; the vehicles speed along the illuminated expanse, the loudspeakers overstrain themselves, transmitting something similar to poetry. I have no strength to run, to stand, or to look.

It lasts an hour, it lasts two, three . . .

"Comrade controller! Allow me to sit in a vehicle. I'm a correspondent, I need to look around."

The controller looked me over suspiciously, but a fountain pen was sticking out of my pocket, and this saved me.

"Sit down. Two trips."

"Zakharych. I'll be with you'."

The "MAZ" started with a jerk, and there am I, my heart standing still, hanging about in the cab on the bridge. A girl with a little flag motions the vehicle toward her. Zakharych obeys her like a schoolboy. The bridge rocks like the deck of a ship. When it swings down, my heart stops, and I feel a bit queasy. "Shukh-shukh-kh-kh!" Splashes, murk—and instantaneously a pure mirror of water.

"Doesn't it get carried away?"

"Indeed it does! Our rocks are now at Irkutsk itself . . ."

"Zakharych! Why do they dump?"

"We'll dump until we overcome. Either we overpower it, or it overpowers us."

"Zakharych?"

"What did you think? We're playing with trifles?"

158

"Is it true you'll work for 24 hours?"

"Voluntarily. Whoever wishes to. Maybe more . . ."

"And rest?"

"What rest?"

I'm in Zakharych's cab for the first time. I clutch the handles, hold on to the door, but almost bump my head on the roof. It shakes. It turns you inside out. The roar of the motor, the smell of gasoline. The hands on the lighted dials jump. Zakhar Zakharych turns the steering wheel furiously, leans out the window, shouts something.

"Well, you are doing work!"

"Our usual work, Tolia."

"How can you endure it?"

Before my eyes, as in a kaleidoscope, passes the excavator bucket, a torrent of rocks into the dumper, the wobbly strip of road, the crowd at the bridge, the aquamarine water, the yellow bubbles, and again the excavator bucket. So quickly, so swift. My temples are throbbing, I feel dizzy. I'm already drunk.

"What is surprising," says Zakhar Zakharych, "is that we work today without norms, without records. Drivers are the type of people that unless they are given credit for a trip, they won't raise a finger, they won't even move the vehicle. But now look at what they're doing. Each strives to move ahead, each strives to do more and faster. No one will know how much each of them has transported. We work like an artel! And they are making headway. You don't know why not a single one refused to work 24 hours? All, all of them as one man! So what is it? You understand that if they were to tell us to throw ourselves in the water right now—Good Lord, you'd find those who would throw themselves to barricade it with their vehicles!

And I do believe this! But I can't think—I'm tired from the jolting. I jump out on the bridge.

"Aha! This is where you fall into my clutches!" I had fallen right into the embrace of Misha Ol'khonskii. He carried a tape-measure. "You see what's going on? And? Is Siberia so bad? If you want, I'll throw you down there?"

For an instant a savage gleam lit up in his eyes, something Genghis Khan-like, and I felt uneasy, but only for a moment. Misha already was shouting, his eyes shining joyously:

"The speed of the current has increased! Do you understand, you helpless fellow, you understand nothing!"

He ran on, forgetting about me. I leaned over the edge of the bridge and looked into the green abyss. Sparkles of spectral light appeared from time to time, a spotlight groped about in the depths of the water, and it suddenly shone through . . . The bottom wasn't visible. Soon it would be midnight. Staggering, straining so as not to fall under the wheels, I left the bridge and settled on the gravel of the slope. Some in the crowd began to remark:

"The blocks have arrived. The blocks!"

STILL THE BATTLE

That's when it started, the main event! Up to now it had been a reconnaissance. Now the cranes began to rumble, new dump trucks advanced in a column. The first concrete block fell into the water like a cannon shot. A fountain of splashes flew high up, the block was turned over, tossed up, and carried away like a matchbox. They moaned indistinctly on the shore: the Angara carries away concrete!

The blocks splashed in one after another. Every single dump truck had switched over to the blocks. Large, small, oblong blocks—they are conveyed to the bridge, and the cannon shots over the river resounded like a cannonade. One understands nothing of what's going on in the middle of the river. The deceptive water sometimes, it seems, shows a block lying somewhere in the depths, but when you look carefully—it's a play of light, nothing more. Shots, shots, shots . . . It's long past midnight. Nearly the entire settlement is on the shore. There in the crowd I've encountered Oktiabrina, Valia Sereda and Vovka, Kubyshkin and Galia, Tamarka—all of whom I know. And everyone is excited, and no one goes home.

160

Some leaflets printed in red are distributed. Alarming rumors: one of the bridge hawsers had broken. Were the bridge to collapse, everything would fall, and scarcely anyone on the bridge would be rescued . . .

Aquamarine water. Aquamarine water . . .

And suddenly shouts, a moan from the crowd:

"It's in sight! It's in si-ght!"

The next block, having plunged into the water, had not disappeared into the depths, but like a miracle lay on the surface right in the middle of the river. What's holding it? Why the miracle? I begin to understand that the barricade of blocks already had reached the surface. This first block protrudes from the water like a broken tooth, with breakers around it; it seems to roll, now it disappears like a mirage. No, it lies there. It is lying there!

They dump, and dump again. Now the bridge has raised slightly; as though it hangs on a slope, waters surrounding a rampart—and in the center of the rampart a tooth, a broken tooth! The Angara rolls through the barricade, rises higher and higher, the hawsers creak. Beneath the bridge there is already a continuous waterfall.

"The second one can be seen! It's in sight!"

THE BATTLE CONTINUES

It was very quiet and peaceful in our yard. A lantern which Pet'ka had hurriedly affixed to a pillar shone weakly, and mysterious shadows moved about, practicing witchcraft over something. Cube-shaped holes were dug in the ground; the dump trucks fill them with concrete, and it hardens there.

The headquarters announced: more than a thousand blocks were needed. The reflooding will require more than 24 hours. A turning point had come, but the Angara would rise and stand on end and the drivers will pour.

"Tonia, good evening!"

"Are you asleep? It's already good morning! Why don't you rest, you clown, you're in the 8:00 a.m. shift."

"How can one sleep when such things are going on!"

"Tol'ka, my dear!" Dashka greeted me, "Take over for me, tamp a little! You, lazybones, took a breather, and we haven't seen anything. For five minutes! Replace me!"

"All right!"

"Only watch what you're doing, no hack-work, you so-and-so! The tamper is weak, don't knock it around."

From far away came a rumble. The cannonade was continuing: the headlight beams and spotlights pierced through the smoke. It resembled a great conflagration: the smoke, the glow, the silhouettes of people rushing about.

Tonia and I, shoulder to shoulder, place the tampers into a hole, and the concrete quivers, bubbles, and swims.

"How boring to be alive if everything already had been built . . ."

"That will never be," said Tonia.

"But is that good?"

"It is."

"Tonia . . . Truly?"

"Yes."

"How do you always know what I'm talking about?"

"Because I think about the same things. I've already told you that."

She had never told me this, but it seemed to me this was so; I felt as though we had had a complicated argument, invisible, unseen, but sharp.

"Today you're alone. Alone, just as at the dances and at the block."

She looks at me, and suddenly I understand that I'm drawing toward her, and she likewise understood this and each waits and is afraid. Were I to embrace her now, she wouldn't utter a word, she'd continue to look, and were I to kiss her . . .

I reeled toward her, grasped her arm at the elbow, her warm, live arm

"Ton'ka! Ton'ka! Where are you?"

Dashka ran along the boards, behind her Valia Sereda pulled her Vovka by the hand, admonishing:

162

"Don't whine, don't whine to me or I'll spank you! You may lie about until evening, but mama must go to work. We'll stroll together. Girls, is the car coming soon? Vovka and I are leaving! Tell auntie 'bye-bye'."

Tonia rushed to the little boy, frowning, and looking hurt; she busied herself with him, and wiped his nose. Dasha looked at us suspiciously and said indifferently:

"Go now. I've seen enough."

Something was throbbing within me. I sat in the cab of the truck, Valia sat with Vovka, and how glad I was that Vovka was whimpering and distracting her; I looked into the distance at the glow, at the solitary lantern of our yard. The road wound among the potholes and poles, and the glow appeared on the right, sometimes on the left.

CONTINUATION OF A LEGEND

Valia and Vovka lived on the second floor of a wooden house in a tiny corner room. There was barely enough space for a bed, the cradle, a little table, and a chair. Various finery and celluloid toys were scattered about; bread crumbs on the table lay higgledy-piggledy with books, a mirror, and little bottles of medicines.

I didn't need to go to her place, but I couldn't resist and she dragged me persistently, as though something, God knows what, depended on me having tea. Or did she want to tell me something important?

"This is how we live. Luxurious, isn't it? Excuse me for not having picked it up—there was no time. Vovka's in nursery school all day, I'm at work; we only sleep at home."

"Valia, do you have relatives?"

"No, they've died. I'm alone."

"Alone?"

"But I'm not crying. What's there to cry about? To howl for every occasion—there aren't enough tears; one would have to drink a pail of water a day, like a horse . . . Vovka, don't put the comb in your mouth! Don't I have a fine son, Tolia? Now, let me blow your nose once more. Again! Oh you, my joy, my sorrow! Well, let's sit down, hup!"

She poured tea for herself, for Vovka, for me. She drank it down, became pensive.

"We live alone . . . there's no daddy. That's how it is, Tolia, among your brothers there are . . . bad ones. We girls are stupid, trusting, we give everything, but he . . . Don't rush to embrace the girls, Tolia, don't play around. But if you love one, don't hurt her, don't cast her off, I beg you! Listen, I beg you!"

She said this so passionately, so hotly, that I involuntarily started.

"Do you understand me?"

"Yes."

"Vovka! Don't pour it on the table cloth! Well? You don't want it? To sleep? Say 'good night' to uncle."

Vovka was naughty, whined, lay on the bed and didn't want to sleep.

"Mama, the cars, the cars"

"He saw a lot, the poor boy, and now isn't sleepy," Valia said with annoyance. "He is very impressionable."

Through the little window the glow was visible; it seemed the noise of the cannonade even reached to here, or was it the sound of the wind?

"Well, don't you want to sleep? I told you we should go home earlier. No, 'don't want to, don't want to!' Listen, I'm going to tell you about the Little White Steer."

"I don't want it."

"So what do you want?"

"About the Angara."

"I've already told it to you twice."

"Again!"

Whereupon Valia, quietly rocking the little bed, began to tell about the beautiful Angara, the grey-headed Baikal, the hero Enisei, and the awesome Shaman Rock.

164

She finished, but Vovka wasn't asleep.

"Again!" he demanded anxiously and naughtily.

"That's all, my little son; go to sleep, my dear."

"No, that's not all!"

"It's not all? I've told you everything."

"Not everything."

"Well, O.K., you win . . . Don't fuss . . . Listen."

I too listened (and then wrote this story down from memory). It was—

The End of a Story

. . . thus the beautiful Angara and the handsome Enisei lived for thousands and thousands of years.

They were happy, as only the most beautiful and audacious people might be. They luxuriated on lissom beds among the hills and flowers, splashed at daybreak, and Angara scattered about her iridescent diamond splashes.

Once a man came. He told Angara and Enisei:

—To live only by luxuriating and picking flowers, to live only by scattering diamond splashes—this still isn't happiness. I know another happiness, the greatest on earth, and I'll give it to you. Stop!

Angara laughed, and Enisei smiled into his jet-black moustache. Who knew how to teach them how to live? Who was wiser and mightier than they?

Then to their shore came many, many people. They had decided to stop with force those who didn't believe them.

They began to throw rocks into the water. Angara frothed, and boiled, and carried away the rocks like light feathers. But the people went on throwing. Angara was courageous, but they were more so; Angara was recalcitrant, but they were more so!

They forced Angara and Enisei to work. To provide light, joy, and warmth for people.

Then a miracle happened.

Then Angara and Enisei understood that until then their happiness had been slight; they knew and had seen nothing of life.

Because whosoever does not toil, does not work, but merely scatters diamond splashes—has understood nothing in life. Because to work, to bring joy, light and warmth—this is the very greatest, the very largest, joy on earth.

Real happiness—is happiness in work.

AN EVENT IMMATERIAL FOR HISTORY

Finally I received my pay. The advance payment I had missed while in hospital, so therefore I got everything at once. Latterly I had had money. Our Zakhar Zakharych, it turned out, is a millionaire from whom one may always borrow. He's alone, earns a good deal, and gladly helps everyone. He found some poor lady watchman with four children, she does his laundering, and he helps her to make ends meet. Pet'ka unscrupulously borrows from him for chemicals. Should the photographic chronicle of the construction site ever appear, you will know that this fundamental undertaking was financed completely by Zakhar Zakharych. When a debt is repaid to the old man, he's always genuinely surprised: "Are you sure you borrowed from me?"

Having received my money, I lost my head with joy. I simply had never held such a bundle in my hands. I carried it in my fist—which is somehow shameful and awkward. I put it in my pocket—my trousers bulged.

At first, of course, I repaid my debts: to Nikolai, the girls, Zakharych. I forgot one of the girls, and one tenner was left over. No matter who I asked, no one would take it. Then I sent three hundred rubles to mother. I put aside some for food. And there remained four hundred rubles.

I decided to buy a watch. Never in my life had I owned one. How I had envied others! Vic had worn a watch since the fifth grade. Zakharych, Tonia, Len'ka—all have watches. No, winter is still far off, the coat can wait, I'll buy a watch.

Mishka Ol'khonskii also had to be in Irkutsk, and he offered to help me.

166

We travelled together on a passing cutter, "The Eagle " placed at the stern among the coils of rope and the fire buckets.

The six gantry cranes slowly vanished in the smoke. The station, flooded by water, was low and split the breakers. The viaduct trembled and vibrated; boards were spread over the apertures of shafts so that no one unexpectedly stumbled in—if one fell in the water, that's the end of you: you would be carried away into the spiral chambers, into the rotor wheels. For sport fishermen it was a holiday. When free from work, they crawled along the ledges at the discharge gates soaked by splashes and caught the stunned, weakened fish with home-made nets.

Where is the aquamarine water? There is none! Brown, muddy, restless, for a whole week it has carried silt and rubbish from the foundation ditch, gouged the bottom of its new bed, torn out roots and grass. Such a change in a river's life is no joke! It has lost its cold, blinding brilliance because of this.

I remember in my childhood when we visited my grandmother in the village that we children "made a little road." We went to a little brook; formed a hill of sand with our hats, hands, and small chips of wood; threw stones into the brook, and then caved in the sand—hurriedly trampled it down and reinforced it. And for half an hour the brook suddenly stopped, spreading a muddy pool in the gully. We jumped, yelled, and waded knee-deep in the "deep water." What bliss!

Bliss! What a miracle—to know that you're taking part in something real, that you're working concrete higher and higher, that you are standing on your feet above the seething Angara on a viaduct, and if you have any concerns today—it's the purchase of a watch.

"You, Mishka, are a remarkable person. But you're a *stiliaga*."

Mishka examined his suit with surprise, his new shoes with rubber soles, and suddenly began to scold me:

"Fool! You nonentity! You only know how to jabber nonsense! In your view every well-dressed person is a *stiliaga*. A *stiliaga* is a social phenomenon. Ask him: whence did he get it? At whose expense does he live? What does he seek in life? A *stiliaga* is not rubber soles on one's feet, it's a rubber-sole heart!"

"Oh, Mishka, you've a remarkable yap: as you open it, out rushes the thesis of a report. Obviously, only the grave will reform you. Should I throw you down there?"

"Hold it, don't muss my suit . . ."

"Aha, the *stiliaga* is frightened! O.K., we'd best discuss what sort of watch I should buy."

We spent half a day in the shops. We went through all the commission stores and mercilessly rejected the goods displayed there. Gold watches we rejected at once as a survival of capitalism and, moreover, they cost more than a thousand. A pocket watch—is a pure prejudice. A "Star" is too cheap, not chic. The "Victory" is old-fashioned. The "Kama", the "Maiak," and others are fashionable but lack—spirit! We bought a "Moskva" for four hundred rubles exactly, 16 jewels, small with a golden face, green luminous numbers, and a sweep second hand. It was actually a small stop-watch! The Second Watch Factory in Moscow, the one on the Leningrad Highway. There is a stop there for trolleybus nos. 12 and 20. When you ride to "Dinamo" the conductor announces "Belorussian Station," next stop—"The Second Watch Factory" . . .

Places dear to my heart come to mind . . . It's from there, from Moscow, my watch, assembled there by some girl who doubtless is hurrying to the canteen or is descending the subway escalator and doesn't know where the watch is now or who is holding it in his hands. We will build the hydroelectric station, leave, and someone will walk along the highway on its crest, rub the wall with his hand—and not know where the people have gone who had smoothed it there—even if their fingerprints are visible!

In the Historical Museum on Red Square I have seen broken clay pieces of pottery from the Neolithic age; I've forgotten everything, but one thing sticks in my memory: the impressions of fingers on a pot—from the fingers of a person who lived seven thousand years ago . . .

. . . That same evening we organized an enormous binge in the hostel. Tamarka and Tonia came. We were sorry Zakhar Zakharych didn't. We'd have been glad to have him! He had left for the night shift. Leonid brought his gramophone, but Misha didn't like his records and dragged over a suitcase of tangos, waltzes, and foxtrots. Well, I said he's a *stiliaga!* And Russian songs—these we sang when we parted.

Pet'ka immortalized us at the festive table, cautioning that even though the light was sufficient the snaps might not come out because of a new improvement in the camera which he was now testing. I was worried that the sleeves of my jacket were too long and tried to keep my left hand on the table. We smoked a lot, it was hot, stuffy. Tonia got up and went out on the porch. I went out, approached her . . . embraced and kissed her.

She trustfully pressed against me, defenceless, tender, shuddered from the night freshness, and suddenly began to sob. This was so unexpected. I stood there, a bit confused, but knew that this was needed, and she cried as though she had been in an agony of suspense for a long time and had sorrows, hardships, difficulties; she cried and patted my shoulder.

Misha Ol'khnonskii came out, yawned, looked at the starry sky, and said:

"Oh, you're here. Well, O.K."

And left.

A LETTER FROM VIKTOR

"Hi, joker!

Interesting that you don't answer my letters. Perhaps, old man, you've become a high-principled comrade? Working on your biography? I find it amusing. By the way, in our world, the Virgin Lands or Siberia are the most desirable (and convincing!) points of an autobiography, as my brilliant pop says.

Well, Tolia, in this respect you are perhaps right. In life one must play for big stakes, and without sentiment. If you understand this, I'm happy for you. Life is a wilderness. People are wolves, jackals. If you stand gaping or act in defiance of them, they'll simply chew you up.

What honor for devils is the "construction of a radiant future"! Each builds only his own prosperity. I think you're convinced of this. Start to climb in your work!

Your worker forbears wanted to spit on that "radiant future." Money and an apartment, devour and drink—that's all they were interested in. Animal life. I look forward to what you'll tell me when we meet. I hope it will be soon?

Well, I'll write about myself. I've been admitted to the technical school. But it was a close squeak. Papa and mama in their joy promised me a motor-scooter. A wonderful thing—and not so expensive. We'll drive, Tol'ka! I've even gone to the shop and looked at them. I'll tell you confidentially that my parent has undertaken one venture, and if it comes off, we'll have the surplus value for the scooter!

Meanwhile, I've acquired a "Iauza" tape recorder to record jazz from the radio. Oh, Tolia, "boogie-woogie" is prehistoric crap; we ventured to try "rock and roll" on one occasion, which they say is stupendous. In Moscow rubber-soled slippers have appeared—they're a dream! They are tailoring me a suit of imported material. In short, I'm beginning to look human.

Among other things, old man, I've thought of getting married. That doesn't hurt in life, they say, you know. Iuna, it seems, is not opposed, but she has, as always, a legion of admirers. But you know me, I know how to flatter.

Well, stay healthy and for heaven's sake drop me a line at last so I know you're alive. I'm terribly interested to know how you're doing. Try to return soon, we'll carouse together "with merry comrades, otherwise known as rabble," as is sung in some underworld song. You know in our circle now it's a sign of good taste to sing thieves' songs. It's exotic!

"Ignoble Mus'ka, you loved me . . ."

Life, Tolia, life is a game! Don't lose time, youth passes on. Make the most of it!"

SEAMEN DIE AT SEA

In the morning there was terrible news: our Zakharych was dead.

He had died at night, about to take the shift, while adjusting the motor. All the dump trucks had driven out, but Zakharych's "MAZ" for some reason stood still. The controller hailed him—he didn't answer. They approached— but the old man already was cold at the wheel: his heart had stopped.

That morning the door to our room hardly ever closed: Zakharych, it turned out, had so many acquaintances, so many people were shaken by his death; they came running—many we had never laid eyes on before—and kept asking, as though we knew something.

They decided not to move Zakhar Zakharych to the hostel. One of the drivers came to take his suit; they dressed the old man there, in the garage, in the Red Corner. When Pet'ka and I arrived there, he already lay on tables pushed together—peaceful, with gnarled hands badly laid out on his chest: his hair again seemed to me to be as dull as a snow-white pillow.

The chairs were arranged in the corner of the Red Corner, and it was rather dark and bleak; people came and went constantly, heels clicking. There was a guard of honor; no one cried.

In the corner the trade union organizer conversed in whispers with the drivers about a red cloth, a little pillow for the Orders, and a coffin:

"But let's take the slab to the repair depot, I've already arranged it . . . And you, Nekhoda, you'll drive tomorrow, do you hear; make your vehicle so that it looks like a hearse, lower the side, drive in first gear . . ."

"I know . . ."

"Ivan Stepanovich! Burgov says the cloth should be removed from the tables only to be returned!"

"Be careful, don't get them dirty. How shall we carry the banner? . . .

Pet'ka and I stood around, silent, and it seemed to us that we were alien and superfluous, and our "old man" was no longer ours. There he lay, and he was no more. We went home . . .

The funeral took place on the next day. An enormous crowd of people assembled, and again no one cried. The club amateur orchestra played out of tune; the day was overcast; a raw wind fluttered the banner, tucked up the red cloth on the truck, and laid bare indelible spots. The driver couldn't keep formation with those who were walking. The procession suddenly broke up and shouted: "Wait!" The groups of people at the gates were talking:

"What sector was he from?"

"Not from a sector, from the garage. Do you remember, he transported the pipes to our yard?"

"That's him?"

"Yes."

"That's how it is: there was a man, and he is no more . . ."

In the hills the construction people had laid the beginnings of a small cemetary—about ten mounds. A strange, unbearable feeling depresses me when I am in the presence of such remote Siberian cemeteries, where tempestuous heads and restless hearts found the end of their journey, brought there, heaven knows how, as exploiters of the land. And I remembered how the old worker had once said: builders come and go, and they leave behind them not merely a station but also dozens of graves. Seamen die at sea, and builders at construction sites.

The superintendent picked up Zakharych's bedding; the bare iron bed stood there. Pet'ka and I grew quiet and tried not to look at that corner. Zakharych had left behind only an empty suitcase, a razor, and an unfinished library book, *The Seekers.*

It must be said that I was only aware of everything that had happened for the first time several days later.

I was returning from the shift, exhausted, foaming, sat down to rest in the grass, on the slope, near the wooden stairway. The red setting sun was shining; groups of workers were hurrying home; the dump trucks were rum-

172

bling and turning below. There was a smell of dust, iron; the construction site was clattering and ringing, as always. I looked about and became thoughtful.

Zakharych . . . A man . . . He had given his all to life, without holding back. He had acquired nothing and left no belongings behind. He drove a tank in the Revolution, built factories, hauled ammunition at Leningrad, poured blocks into the Angara—to this he had given all of himself.

Below, beneath me, the river flows in a new channel, the walls are standing—how can one find out or distinguish what Zakhar Zakharych had done? But, nonetheless, here is what he did with his own hands!

His monuments stand throughout the entire country—everywhere!—nameless, enormous, alive. What is the little mound in the hills? A mere conventionality? Zakhar Zakharych isn't there, he's everywhere in the hum and movement of life.

Could I be like him? There's Misha Ol'khonskii, Leonid the Siberian, or—I've just remembered!—Dima Strepetov, Ivan Bugai, and Vasek—they will be. But Grishka the greedy? And Leshka—the good-natured thief? What monument will remain after them? A pile of stolen glasses and a deck of cards . . . And Vic who has found "the treasure of life"? . . .

A LYRICAL DIGRESSION

Wayfarer passing through the station, traveller or tourist or artist, if sometime you see the Irkutsk Hydroelectric Station, ride in a train run on its power or read a book in the light it provides—know that these grey walls, these piers and waste-gates placed across the Angara and raising it 30 meters, were made by us, the concrete workers, with our own hands.

Len'ka the Siberian dug the ground and built the concrete forms, Kubyshkin tied up the steel reinforcement, Pet'ka the photographer installed the lighting system, and Zakhar Zakharych hauled the crushed stone; our strong and happy girls put in the concrete, and Tonia watered it with a hose, Dasha carefully wrapped it with tarpaulin.

173

We suffered from thirst and heat in the summer and froze in winter, we burned bonfires at night; poured concrete on the viaduct; made defective rejects, repaired them, received banners, told children the legend. We yearned for apples, and our hands ached.

This has been our life—I say ours because I became a real builder and can not imagine myself as anything else.

The station enters into the network, and we pack our belongings. Red Nikolai hoists his folding chairs on to his shoulder. Valia takes Vovka out of the nursery school—and we depart. Thus, since I've left my home for a long trip, I'll travel on and on . . .

"Our locomotive, fly ahead . . ."

Perhaps we'll go on to the Bratsk Hydroelectric Station where my far-away Dima Strepetov, Ivan Bugai, and Vasek have pitched their tents and are cutting pine trees and hauling beams—tongues hanging out of their mouths. There are no concrete jobs there yet, but there will be when we arrive.

We'll meet again, Dimka! We'll study together again, Ivan, at an Institute—keep your textbooks. I don't have your addresses, only your surnames, but I firmly believe that we'll meet because the paths of builders do cross.

As for you, Vic, we'll not meet . . . If you do graduate from your trade technical school, you won't come out here in any event, you'll set up in the capital through pull. Your good papa won't begrudge the money. You'll live like a wolf all your life and never find out whether there is real life in the world. Oh, I find this offensive: what's happened to you and who did this to you? Whence such filth, such cowardice?

I can not write to you: it's very difficult for me. The first letter you sent to me has lain in my heart like a stone. Don't wait for me in your strange wilderness; your mama isn't awaiting a cedar cone. I can't respond to you with a single word, I've written memoirs. They—in all truth, in all sincerity and

174

pain—are the answer to you. And if someone regards these memoirs as a challenge, he'll not be mistaken. So, get ready!

We will destroy the wolves. Everything in the world is just beginning! Many struggles face us in life. Our generation is only entering into them.

We are taking the baton from Zakhar Zakharych. Listen to that, you builders of your own dachas! Listen to that, you snivellers who panic when confronted by a mess!

Yes, it seems I've become somewhat more mature because I'm beginning to understand something . . . People become truly mature when they comprehend what life is all about. Life! No, it doesn't belong to you, snivellers and cowards. Life belongs to people who do not build their own well-being exclusively. They are the salt and the pride of the earth. Without them you would be lost within twenty-four hours, and they'll sweep you away with a broom! They have sunny hearts, and hands—oh, strong, muscular, full of bloody blisters. Those hands are capable of building a wonderful life, and no one, nothing, will ever be able to stop its coming!

THE BEGINNING OF THE NEXT NOTEBOOK

ON THE ROAD

No sitting around! The laundry awaits at home, and if my photographer is on a drinking spree, cooking dinner too. I was hurrying toward the hostel when someone called to me:

"Hey! Old pal! How's life, lad?"

The first things I saw were gold teeth. My "self-seeker" was in a brand spanking new cheviot suit, felt hat, and custom-made shoes.

"You obviously are calling on someone?" I smiled.

"Almost. There's to be a christening party at my house. So my women have sent me to the shop."

He held a woven basket in his hands out of which protruded a dozen and a half bottle–necks sealed with sealing-wax.

"Milk for the kids?"

"Ha, ha, ha! You are a bright lad!" He laughed with sincere satisfaction, slapping me heavily on the shoulder. "Well, come on over to my place."

"Really! Dressed like this . . ."

"Never mind! We're all workers, only our own people. Let's go!" He whispered: "Listen, I'll introduce you to a girl. What lips!"

"Thank you, no. I don't want to. I'm tired."

"As you wish. But it's a pity. We'll still work together. So long. We'll meet again!"

Yes . . . we'll meet again.

At home, happily, Pet'ka had cooked dinner. On the bed in the corner there already was fresh, snow-white bedding, and on it sat a new person.

Thus, in place of Zakhar Zakharych an absolutely genuine, one-hundred percent Ukrainian had moved in, black eyebrows, stately, dark-complexioned, and already scolding in Ukrainian:

"What do I need these photographs for! If you want to make more of them, get out of the house."

"O.K." said Pet'ka, sipping his cabbage soup. "See here, Vasyl', if you're going to fuss, I'll take colored ones. I'll poison you to hell."

"Go on, you little devil, I'll poison you myself."

"Well, well, hold your tongue, son. I'll wipe your nose."

"Wipe your own. If you want to take pictures, go into the corridor, get lost there, but don't hang them in my window!"

"Who do you think you are? This is boorishness: to appear in someone else's room and immediately introduce your own rules. We'll throw you out!"

"Who? You? Try it! Come on!"

Pet'ka began to roll up his sleeves. I arrived just in time to make him sit down again. Vasyl' started to complain that he already had changed rooms three times—and always fell in with a photographer, but he is studying to enter a technical school and needs light and quiet. Five minutes later he was shouting about something else:

"You lazybones! You pigs! This place is becoming a pigsty and you just sit around like idiots! Why are your trousers lying on the table. You have a wardrobe, don't you?"

178

Then he nagged us because we didn't take off our boots outside, which makes the place stuffy. Pet'ka and I only exchanged a glance: "Wow-w . . ."

Vasyl' lay down, covered his head, then leapt up at once and, sitting on the bed, shouted and jabbered, to our indescribable horror, all evening. He disclosed that he's a carpenter and has the ability to read and write, that he's studying at a technical school by correspondence, showed us his books, notebooks, exercise books, informed us that he has "a girl in the Ukraine fairer than all others in the world," and read aloud a letter from his old mother who lives in the village of Starye Petrivtsy: "Dear son! I'm also sending you some lard and more than 30 pears. I'm very worried that you're not eating properly . . ."

"But where's the lard?" Pet'ka inquired.

"Oh, I've already eaten it."

This damned Vasyl' had arrived—everything has been turned inside out and he'd worked us up. We turned off the light but didn't feel like sleeping. We lay in the darkness, silent, and then Pet'ka asked hesitatingly:

"And what documents does one need for a technical school?"

Vasyl' jumped out of his bed like a bomb. In his bare feet he rushed first to the switch, turned on the light, and standing in the middle of the room, cried out:

"Oh, to hell with you cowards. Aren't you a fool not to have thought of that earlier? You're an electrician, you should study on and on! You need to study while you're young, but then no one's forcing you to pick up a book. Get up, parasite, there are so many roads before you, dig in! Get up, write your application. Get up, get up!"

He pulled off the blanket, threw pillows. Pet'ka blinked his eyes and scratched his neck. They sat around the table and began to plan Pet'ka's life. Happily my turn didn't come that night.

But I myself couldn't fall asleep until dawn and thought: what should I do? After school it was so awful, but now roads truly had opened to me everywhere. What had happened to my eyes and to me? No, of course I wouldn't remain simply a concrete worker. Next year I'll apply to the correspondence

179

construction institute. I have production practice, I can study in the winter, review everything, and master German.

"I need to get textbooks," I thought, "and to buy an alarm clock. I must learn not to get tired at work; after the shift there must be a second full working day: I need to sit down in the evenings under an electric light, read new books, not miss the films and the newspapers, learn to get ready more quickly in the morning, and to be satisfied with six hours of sleep."

Study, study! . . . Many long years. I wanted to leap up at once and run out, buy notebooks, ink, my hands were itching: I have been missing all that! . . .